Home Grown Food

BY MILO SHAMMAS
Dr. Earth

CEDAR HOUSE
PRESS

CEDAR HOUSE PRESS
Vacaville, California

Cedar House Press
Vacaville, California 95687

Milo Shammas

Library of Congress Cataloging-in-Publication Data
Home Grown Food
Includes index.
Library of Congress Control Number: 2015932122
ISBN 978-0-692-37896-0

Printed in the United States of America
Walsworth Publishing Company
Marceline, Missouri 64658

Designed by Colortek
Book Jacket: Tom Zipp • Book Layout: Jody Goetz & Megan Webb
Set in Cambria

Disclaimer of Liability
This book offers information and recommendations on the general relationships among food, human and animal health, and disease prevention. Some information is based on the author's personal and professional experiences. Additional information on the composition and contents of foods and the results of research on the health effects of various foods in one's diet come from sources the author and publisher believe to be reputable and accurate. However, each person has his or her unique biochemical makeup and health history. Whether the reader should use any fact, recommendation or inference in this book as a guide to his or her own health or the health of any other person is strictly a matter of personal choice and responsibility. Results may vary from one person to another. THIS BOOK IS NOT A SUBSTITUTE FOR QUALIFIED MEDICAL DIAGNOSIS AND TREATMENT. The author and publisher take no responsibility and cannot be held liable for the consequences to the reader of acting or failing to act on anything written here.

I dedicate this book to my wife, Patricia.
She is my everything. I cherish every day we grow together.

Contents

Acknowledgements

A book, like a company, has two elements: the concept and the execution. This book comes from the collaboration of an excellent team who took my concept of how to grow your own food at home and made it real in this book.

Megan Webb, my book and website designer, always gives me tasteful, elegant and top quality design that truly reflects what I am feeling.

Tom Zipp, my dear friend and lead designer, takes the conceptual blubber out of my head, and makes it very real and beautiful.

Jody Geotz, a perfectionist through and through, keeps all my designer ideas tight and accurate.

As always, my family who helped to form me and continue to inspire me to create a better tomorrow.
My father, Lou, funded my dream of starting Dr. Earth when I was a young 25 year old man with a big dream.
My mother, Jeanette, loves me more than life itself.
My big brother, Nick, one of the most talented people ever.
My big sister, Rouba, one of the gentlest souls ever.

The Dr. Earth company team, spread across the United States, give me their all every day in pursuit of the organic ideal. Without them, it's still just a big idea.

I love you all deeply from the bottom of my heart.

Introduction

If you are a beginner, wondering if you can develop a "green thumb," you will love organic gardening. Why? Because when you do all the right things, you get satisfying results. Soon after you do the planning and some simple work, you see visible results. Your seeds sprout, your plants grow. Within weeks or months you pick food you grew yourself.

Beyond your health, the joys of gardening include the knowledge you accumulate with every season. This is lifelong learning at its best, because you apply the knowledge to the ground under your feet. And the benefit of that knowledge comes into your kitchen as a healthier, more natural diet.

The biodiversity in your backyard is a natural laboratory with more specimens than a college life sciences department. At home for little cost, you learn about the microbes in the soil, the insects that crawl and fly, the plants you grow and the nutrition they hold.

The garden gives you a reason to continue learning and to keep exercising. It also gives you something to anticipate with excitement. For many gardeners, "Harvest time is party time."

Gardening is based on science not magic. Many years of careful research, close observation and innovation have given us a deep understanding of life down to the molecular level. If you give a plant what it needs in the right amounts (sunshine, water, nutrients and warmth) it will grow. Unless you interfere with it, you cannot stop life.

If you are a veteran gardener, this book can add to your knowledge of why and how the right things you do are right. And why the wrong things are wrong. For example, what makes digging your wet kitchen scraps into the soil a great thing for your garden? What makes a synthetic, liquid fertilizer such a threat to your garden and your health? What makes your local grocery store not a good place to find the most nourishing food?

Whether you are new to the garden or have done it for many years, growing a healthy garden (rather than just a beautiful one) is a most rewarding experience. When people start growing their gardens, their quality of life improves. A healthy garden offers a place for you and your family to share something natural and uplifting, a place you can regularly depend on for both challenge and achievement. When you teach your children to garden, you give them lifelong skills, an appreciation for what and how we feed ourselves and a meaningful way to connect with you and the world.

Gardening gives you more than the activity and the harvest. You become a steward of the earth, one of millions of organic gardeners who want to make the world a better, healthier place to live. What a wonderful feeling when you see how you helped foster a natural process as old as life itself.

Gardening as work can transcend the purely physical to become a spiritual experience. Working with the soil and nurturing plants for food goes back thousands of years. I feel wonderfully connected to the past by remembering my ancestors did the same thing ten thousand years ago. In a sense, my garden links me to all of humanity past and future.

Look at your backyard as a place of worship, a healing ground or a place of nurturing. In churches, synagogues and meditation halls we nurture our souls and connect with a higher power. What else but a higher power makes biology happen?

The garden is like a natural chapel that can heal and connect you to all of life. Many spiritual men loved working in their gardens. Many of the best gardeners I have known or read about were deeply spiritual in their own way.

Grow your own food for the health of your world.

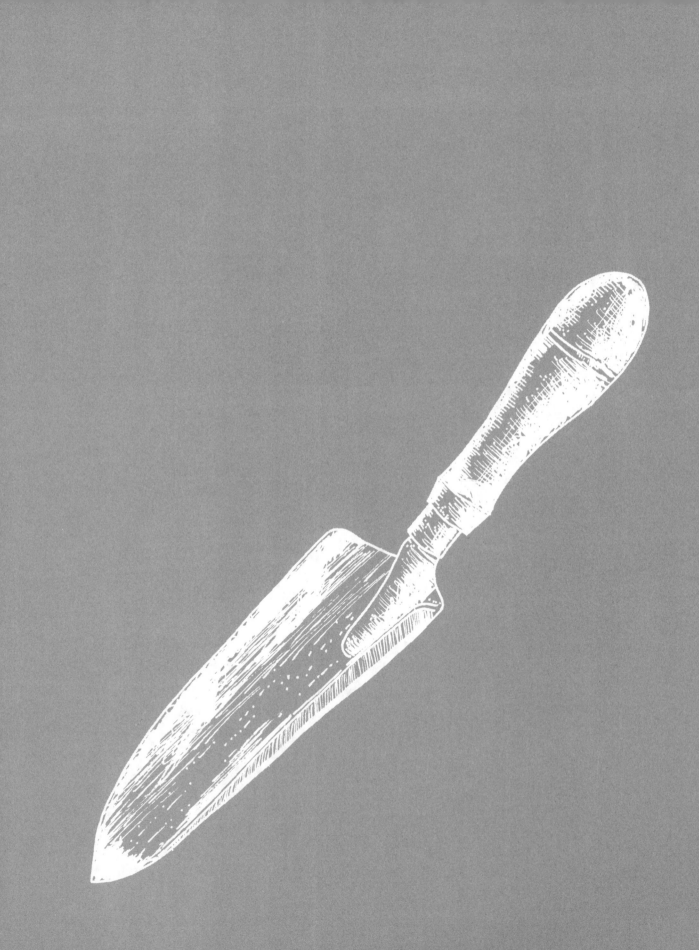

CHAPTER ONE

Life Begins in the Soil (Don't Call it Dirt)

Growing healthy food begins with natural soil where healthy plants get their vitality. Analyze your soil and amend it with organic materials to suit the plants you want to harvest. Read on for the details on how to do it.

You may ask, "How can you call the soil 'natural' when you amend it with something?" Amending your soil returns it to its natural state before the industrial world took the life out.

Plants get their essential nutrients from what lives in the soil. We, in turn, thrive by extracting our essential nutrients from healthy plants that grow in living soil. Whether you plan a quaint home garden or a large urban farm, focus on nurturing the soil. After you analyze your garden and its environment, you will know what you have to work with and what to do next.

Amending your soil returns it to its natural state

Focus on nurturing the soil

TODAY'S SOIL QUALITY AND HOW WE GOT IT

To understand the soil we have today, we need to look into the past. The earliest forms of agriculture began around 10,000 B.C. Nomadic groups of hunter-gatherers settled in the area of the Near East the Greeks called Mesopotamia ("between the rivers.") The Tigris and Euphrates Rivers still flow through what is now modern Iraq.

The nomads found wild barley and wheat growing abundantly. As they learned to plant, cultivate and harvest food, they built villages with a surplus of crops growing nearby.

Chemicals have killed the nutrient value in farm soil

As populations grew, they altered the balance of Nature. They weeded out undesirable plants. They separated domestic animals and crops. They built irrigation systems to divert waterways. They also cleared forests for more space and sunlight. As these industrious, well-fed people multiplied and spread, they demanded an ever-increasing supply of food. The portion of the earth under cultivation grew with the population.

Until well into the 20th Century, most food came from small farms run by individual families using traditional, organic methods. With increasing demand for more and cheaper food to feed a hungry nation (and sell the surplus abroad at a profit), U.S. agriculture grew into a large industrial system. The goal and standard of performance became high yields and high returns on investment.

In the process of consolidation for efficiency, the large farm corporations bought up more than four million U.S. farms that could not compete. After World War II, the U.S. farm population shrank dramatically. In 1960, one farmer fed 25 people. Fifty years later, one farmer fed 129 people. (Source: National Cattlemen's Beef Association.)

To further increase yields at low cost, corporate farming demanded new technologies. Plant scientists at universities and private companies developed chemical fertilizers, herbicides and pesticides.

The increasing use of chemicals has killed the nutrient life in farm soil that supported food crops. Our dead soil is now just an anchor to hold plants. As a result, commercial crops now contain ever-weaker concentrations of essential vitamins, minerals and micronutrients. What was a natural process of agriculture has become unnatural, commercial and a threat to our health.

What happened to degrade our soil? It became one more factor to manipulate in a system that puts profits before people. What to do? Grow your own food free of chemicals.

GET TO KNOW YOUR SOIL

If you look at our abundant plant life, you may wonder:

What makes plants grow large and healthy?
What makes plants wilt or not produce?
How do you get a "green thumb"?

Plants depend on favorable environmental conditions to survive and grow. A healthy plant begins with good genetics suited to its environment. Each plant species then needs its own balance of sunlight, temperature, water and nutrients from healthy soil. Wind, rain and other living organisms also affect a plant's life course.

Any factor out of balance in the equation of life (too much, too little or at the wrong time) can weaken or kill a plant. Nature copes well with soil conditions, ensuring that only suitable plants survive to propagate. But the backyard gardener wants to grow a wider range of plants than local conditions allow. You do this by improving the soil.

What is in soil? About 90 percent of it is non-living solid minerals. Half of that is air space, called pores. The other 10 percent is organic matter. Some living matter grows and expands, such as organisms and roots. Most of the visible biomass is plant roots. While only one-tenth of the soil mass is living matter, it controls plant health. More life in the soil means healthier plants.

As a home gardener, you cannot control the outdoor environment nor plant genetics. Organic growers, in particular, cannot control the genetics of their seeds.

Since so many factors affect plant development, you cannot completely control your results. Instead, control what you can: the health and balance of your soil. Modify it as best you can to cultivate it successfully.

> More life in the soil means healthier plants

IMPORTANT SOIL QUALITIES

To wisely choose the right plants for your environment, you need to know the qualities of your soil. These specific factors also determine the best ways to modify your soil.

The most fertile soils have great consistency and structure for root extension, water retention, and an abundance of organisms living in symbiosis with plants. Two key soil qualities matter most for the home gardener: Composition and pH (the acid-alkaline range.)

Composition

Your garden has one of three basic soil types. Clay has the finest mineral particles and the least amount of air in its structure. Clay soil has such small particles that very little oxygen penetrates it.

To create a more porous texture in clay soil, add organic matter and possibly some grit. Adding gypsum also helps. If the soil is waterlogged and does not drain well, consider installing a drainage system.

In particle size, silt lies somewhere between sand and clay. Silt feels silky. You can often find it in river valleys. If it has lots of organic matter in it, silt makes good garden soil.

Sand has the coarsest mineral particles. Lightweight, sandy soil drains too fast and retains little moisture. Sand needs lots of added organic matter to bind the particles and improve moisture retention. During a drought, plants in sandy soil suffer and often die.

Texture

To the naked eye, soils look much the same. The nature of the soil comes from the underlying rock. In a river valley, water grinds down rock particles to form silt or clay. In areas with only a thin covering, the soil may be rocky or sandy.

To learn what your soil consists of, take a lump in your hand

and crumble it between your fingers. If the soil is sandy, you will hear grains rubbing together and feel them between your fingers. Silt has a soapy feel. Clay is heavy and sticky, with a surface glaze that makes it almost shine.

You will find many different textures in natural soil. Sometimes adding compost or organic fertilizer is not enough to get a beautiful tilth (another name for the ideal state of being cultivated and ready to receive seeds or transplants.) You may need to add grit to get the right texture. Often you must experiment to find the best way to make your soil fertile.

Pores are spaces between soil particles where water and air flow. In the best soil, about half the volume consists of pores. Water and air fill these gaps and attach to the soil particles.

Pore space is crucial to good tilth. Without it, fertilizer will not get into the soil to feed the plants. Also, pores let moisture travel upwards by capillary action.

Loam is what all gardeners aim for, a rich mixture of soil that feels light and friable to the touch and has a pleasant, brown, earthy color. This soil structure has a good combination of organic matter with essential mineral particles, whether they are sand, silt or clay.

Loamy soil encourages earthworm activity and is well aerated. Because it is neither too dense nor too crumbly, loam holds moisture to the right degree with plenty of oxygen for microbes and mycorrhizae, a beneficial fungus. You get loam by generously applying composted material. This creates valuable pore space for roots to travel and accumulate nutrients for their growth.

Microbes that digest organic matter can influence how well a soil holds together. Their activity helps stabilize the soil by binding particles together. Microbes also release a by-product called glomalin that acts like glue for mineral particles and organic matter. Microbial activity helps build the right soil structure by creating semi-stable aggregates.

Often a gardener must experiment to find the best way to make his soil fertile

pH value affects nutrient uptake

pH (Acid-Alkaline Range)

pH is an essential consideration not visible in the soil. Proper pH promotes plant growth by helping roots absorb essential nutrients.

pH stands for parts of Hydrogen, a measure of acidity and alkalinity. Acidity means more hydrogen ions. Alkalinity means more hydroxyl ions. The pH scale goes from 0, completely acid, to 14, completely alkaline. Pure water has a pH of 7.0 and is called neutral.

Most edible garden plants grow best in a slightly acidic soil with a pH of 6.5. Some plants prefer alkaline soils. (See the section on 100 easy-to-grow plants for specific pH needs.) The pH value affects nutrient uptake. If the soil pH is not correct, you can give your plants more nutrients, but the roots may not absorb them.

Buy a pH meter at your local nursery. Test the soil in your planting bed at a few random spots and calculate the average pH. The numbers should range between 6.0 and 7.2, with the ideal 6.5 to 6.7. (For more accurate, reliable results, consult an agricultural experiment station or a private lab.)

If your soil is too alkaline, increase the acid level by mixing in peat moss or soil sulfur. Clay soils need more of both.

With acid soil, offset the low pH by mixing in crushed limestone or wood ash. The amount to apply depends on the soil texture and how much you need to change the pH.

For the organic gardener, pH is not usually a problem. Organic materials tend to naturally adjust soils to a slightly acid range. Also, microbes in organic matter help create the right pH environment.

THE LIFE IN YOUR SOIL

Soil is alive with all types and size of essential organisms: bacteria, fungi, algae, earthworms, actinomycetes, mites and springtails, among many others.

Bacteria are essential to plant nutrition. They form an enormous portion of living matter in the soil, weighing more than a ton per acre. Each gram of fertile soil has about one million different species of bacteria just on the surface. Bacteria also exist far below, but they are most active at the root depth of plants, known as the rhizosphere.

Bacteria are decomposers and recyclers. Some decompose naturally occurring organic matter such as dead cells released by roots or other organic plant and animal remains. Through their metabolism, they release carbon dioxide and other nutrients for plants and animals.

Other types of bacteria transform inorganic matter into forms plants can use. These organisms need carbon dioxide to function. Bacteria also provide essential nitrogen through a process called nitrogen fixation. The Rhizobia bacteria, for example, are symbiotic with the legume family, which includes more than 18,000 species. They convert atmospheric nitrogen from its gaseous form to a water-soluble form plants absorb through their roots.

Fungi decompose fallen leaves and digest dead plants and animals. Fungi come in many different species with many different functions. Some work to degrade organic matter in sequence, from tough fibers down to soft, simple matter that yields usable nutrients. Others form mutual relationships with plants by protecting roots from attack by nematodes or other bugs.

Perhaps the most beneficial fungus for plants is mycorrhizae, which forms a symbiotic relationship with roots. The fungi extend their arms (hyphae or filaments) out into the soil to increase the reach of the roots both wider and deeper. Extensive mycorrhizae webs allow an entire plant population to share nutrients.

Actinomycetes also decompose and recycle dead organisms.

Like bacteria, they break down organic matter and convert atmospheric nitrogen into soluble particles plants absorb. They also serve as a source of antibiotic drugs. Actinomycetes help prevent the overgrowth of bacteria and show that even at microscopic levels, nature keeps an ecosystem in balance.

Algae add organic matter to the soil. Blue-green algae fix nitrogen from the air, retaining this critical nutrient for plant growth. Algae improve soil structure by helping soil particles stick loosely together, which enhances water retention and decreases erosion. They are also food for other bugs living in the soil.

Earthworms travel through the soil by burrowing, eating minerals and organic matter as they go. As they move, they perforate and loosen the soil. During digestion, they transform many unusable minerals for plants to use later. The remains of earthworms, or worm castings, are high in nitrogen, phosphorus, potassium, calcium, trace minerals and beneficial bacteria. In their life processes, earthworms create more nutrient-rich, fertile soil with a pH close to neutral. Many earthworms in your yard shows you have good soil.

Along with earthworms, nematodes and pot worms decompose organic matter into humus. In the process, they secrete a sticky substance that helps the soil form nice, cake-like aggregates. Most abundant on or near grassland, prairies and pastures, they feed on plant debris as well as some bacteria that share the topsoil.

Because nematodes feast on insects in the soil, some gardeners use them as a natural form of pest control. In turn, some larger bugs and even mycorrhizal fungi feast on nematodes. Mites and springtails, the most abundant soil dwellers, decompose many types of organic substances. They belong to the arthropods, which have characteristic exoskeletons and jointed legs. Of the arthropods, mites and springtails are the most vital source in creating humus. In the process, they break down everything from nematodes and pot worms to fungus and leaf litter.

Even at microscopic levels, nature keeps an eco-system in balance

Many earthworms in your yard show you have good soil

These are only a few of the billions of organisms in or around your garden. The amount of nitrogen fixed for plants by bacteria, actinomycetes and green algae is double the amount in commercial fertilizers. Nitrogen is already present in the soil naturally. You just need to feed and nurture it.

HUMUS: BLACK GOLD FOR THE GARDENER

When plants die, they appear to rot away as waste. But Mother Nature never wastes anything. Many varieties of microbes and fungi eat dead plants. As they do, they release nutrients back into the soil for future plant generations.

Everything that goes back into the soil helps to build it by providing the essential nutrients where plants need them, at the root zone. You could say plants grow their own soil.

Microbes are crucial to life because they hold the nutrient energy plants captured from the sun as they grew and thrived. Microbes and fungi pass on their accumulated nutrients to the soil as they actively decompose plant remains. These remains in turn decompose as part of the cycle. Life ends in death. Death feeds life. This cycle creates stable humus and helps form rich, healthy soil.

Humus is usually dark brown, spongy and gooey. Some types of humus contain highly soluble molecules that readily break down further, known as active humus, the best for feeding soil microbes. Stable humus, crucial to the physical qualities of fertile soil, resists breaking down, because its large, insoluble molecules bind tightly to clay molecules.

Organic matter gets consumed many times. As microbes and fungus continue to break down the remains of various organisms into simpler compounds more available to plants, they also add stable organic matter to the soil.

Humus also acts as an important reserve between the fresh organic matter from which it comes and the simpler forms of carbon dioxide, water and minerals that return to the soil,

Mother Nature never wastes anything

Life-Death lifecycle creates stable humus

14

sometimes several years later.

Humus formation varies with air temperature. Above 80°F, organic matter decays faster than it is generated. Below 40° F, activity in the soil slows down, building humus reserves for plants to draw on later. Eventually, this digested organic matter transforms into tiny particles of dark humus.

Add both raw and composted organic matter to your garden. This keeps the biology going strong and adds the physical properties to create beautiful, healthy soil.

> Water transports nutrients from soil particles to plant roots

MAKING YOUR SOIL FERTILE
Soil is like people. Fertilizers are the vitamins, wind and rain are the exercise, and sun and shade are the rest.

Organic fertilizers feed the microorganisms in the soil rather than the plants directly, which is how synthetic fertilizers work. You might ask, "What's the difference if my plants grow?"

By feeding the soil (or fertilizing it) you let it build nutrient reserves that roots tap into as needed. Organic fertilizer builds good soil structure, creates pores for roots to extend their reach, helps suppress disease, and supports biological diversity. It also helps maintain a neutral pH to support humus formation, adding minerals and micronutrients to the living soil.

WATER AS TRANSPORT
In childhood, we learn that plants need water. Yet, water is not just for plants to "drink," as we do when thirsty. Instead, water transports nutrients from soil particles to where the roots absorb them. A soil's ability to do this is called the "cation exchange capacity." As this capacity increases in the soil, plants absorb more nutrients.

COMPOST AND MANURE
Well-made compost works like good organic fertilizer, but it

is not as rich in nutrients. Compost is simply (and nutritiously) the decaying remains of dead organisms broken down by the feeding action of microorganisms.

Compost usually comes from yard wastes, grass and plant trimmings, leaves, soil with microbes, and various wet kitchen scraps other than meat. (Why not meat? It attracts four-legged pests that will feast on your ripe fruits and vegetables.) Apply this composted substance to your soil and get great tilth, microorganisms and nutrients.

Healthy, diverse compost also gives a slow, steady and wider range of nutrients for plant health and disease resistance than a short burst of synthetic nutrients. High quality compost can nourish your plants for a year or more. Because compost is constantly breaking down, you must reapply it to sustain the benefits. Four times a year is a perfect recipe.

Caution: Do not use compost made from biosolids or sewage sludge. They can contaminate your soil with toxic levels of heavy metals, unused or outdated drugs flushed down a toilet, and, most dangerously, human pathogens.

Compost is especially valuable if the ground was degraded in the past and never remediated. All our houses were once construction sites. The weight of the building materials and the house compacts the dirt. (Don't call THAT soil.)

Also, the construction workers may have left behind solids that are not biodegradable, such as iron nails, broken glass, concrete mixing debris, aluminum cans, cigarette butts and plastic trash. The toxic liquids can include both paint from brushes and rollers and the solvents used for cleaning. Whether you see it or not, construction debris and waste can contaminate your ground.

Whatever is in the soil, both nutrients and poison, can be absorbed into the edible parts of your plants. If you don't want it in your body, don't let it be in your soil.

Do not use compost made from biosolids or sewage sludge

If you don't want it in your body, don't put it in your soil

Apply premium compost to your clean ground

If your garden plot has never been worked, your first task is to find and remove all you can that does not belong in your soil. It can be hard work with a shovel and a sturdy metal rake (great for your fitness) or you can use a mechanical rototiller. (With all power tools larger than a hedge trimmer, if you have not used it before, hire a professional who can do the job safely.)

Once your ground is as clean as you can make it, apply premium compost you make or buy. To get safe, effective compost, look for a trusted nursery or professional grower who can tell you how to maximize your soil's fertility.

You can avoid the ground contamination problem by growing your crops in raised beds you fill with the soil you want. See Chapter 3, How to Go Organic, for more on how to make and use raised beds.

Manure, or animal waste, is another effective but risky way to add nutrients to your soil. Manure gives a huge boost to soil fertility for large-scale agriculture, but it must first be composted for a long time.

Once composted, manure is a nutrient-rich material to mix with your soil

Manure is not the best choice for a home garden, especially when better alternatives are readily available. Raw manure may release ammonia, which is detrimental to plant health. Never use the waste of a carnivore (meat eater) such as a cat or a dog. It can carry pathogens.

Once composted, manure is a nutrient-rich material to mix with your soil. You can safely apply manure from rabbits, sheep, horses and cows. Just remember to compost it thoroughly before you mix it into the soil.

Chicken manure is a special case. Not all chicken manures are the same. Most retail chicken manure comes from factory farms, where the birds are fed grain from genetically engineered plants or GMOs. (The organic community opposes the use of GMOs in food products because of the unknown long-term, and perhaps unintended, consequences of using them.) Factory farms also use hormones to make poultry ready for market faster. They also use antibiotics to prevent infections fostered in the crowded, unhealthy conditions in the cages. If the chicken manure contains pathogens or toxins, those go into your soil and expose you to disease.

Read the labels on organic fertilizers. Make sure you know the chicken manure and its source. If you raise your own chickens organically, their manure is safe.

Remember to compost manure thoroughly before you use it.

ORGANIC FERTILIZERS AND SOIL AMENDMENTS

These are the best in all ways. They consist of natural ingredients that feed beneficial microbes and help create ideal soil structure. Popular ingredients of organics include:

- Fishmeal
- Alfalfa Meal
- Kelp Meal
- Seaweed Extracts
- Liquid Fish and Seaweed
- Earthworm Castings
- Feather Meal
- Bone Meals
- Blood Meal

The meals and extracts contain organic matter and nutrients, while the bacteria and the symbiotic mycorrhizal fungi convert nutrient sources into forms plants can absorb as needed. Also, mycorrhizal fungi extend the reach of plant roots to acquire more nutrients and water.

Organic fertilizers are also safer than the alternatives, because they have a much lower chance of leaching through the soil to contaminate the water table. With organic fertilizers, nutrients are physically bound into larger pieces of matter lodged in the soil and available so that microbes can free them up for plant use. Organic fertilizers persist and work for many months, because they are part of the living soil.

Organic fertilizers let you work with Nature rather than against it. You use them to recycle organic matter back into

Organic fertilizers let you work with Nature

Direct plant feeding sounds attractive, but it adds nothing beneficial to the soil

the soil rather than discarding it and relying on chemicals. Your local nursery stocks a number of different organic fertilizers and amendments. Some are formulated to feed particular plant categories such as vegetables, while others take an all-purpose approach for a variety of plants.

Fertilizers are generally tested and proven for a specific purpose. Choose a selection specific to your plants.

Whatever you choose, organic fertilizers and amendments are geared for the slow, controlled release of plant food. They are perfect for preparing the soil for upcoming seasons. Organic nutrients are never wasted and never wash away.

CHEMICAL FERTILIZERS: WHY NOT?

Chemical fertilizers are easy to apply and work fast. They feed plants directly, because they mimic natural soil nutrients in a form plants can absorb immediately. What's the problem? Direct plant feeding adds nothing beneficial to the soil. Also, commercially synthesized chemical fertilizers do not have the beneficial soil microbes that feed the plants certain bio-chemicals such as vitamins and antibiotics. Over time, chemical fertilizers deplete the soil of these nutrients.

With chemicals, the soil becomes a dead anchor to hold plants in place. While this approach may have good short-term results with high yields, in the long run it leads to disaster for the earth.

Chemicals make the soil a dead anchor to hold plants

When organic matter is not replaced in the soil, beneficial organisms die out, the soil structure breaks down, and the soil becomes hard, airless and unproductive. Chemically "force-feeding" plants causes soft, sappy growth, making them vulnerable to pests and disease.

With all the protective organisms gone from the soil, the chemical farmer must apply herbicides and pesticides to replace the lost protection of Mother Nature.

In addition to killing off organisms, chemical fertilizers are water-soluble and temporary, often lost through leaching away or conversion to an unusable form, such as nitrogen gas. Unnatural chemicals in the soil get washed away during rain or irrigation and can pollute ground water, streams, lakes and oceans.

Other negative effects of chemical fertilizers:
- Make certain micronutrients and heavy metals, (iron, magnesium and aluminum), more soluble in the soil and more toxic to plant tissues
- Reduce the productivity of bacteria (nitrogen fixers) making nutrients less available
- Decrease a soil's ability to hold onto positively charged nutrients, making it easier for water to wash them away
- Lock up other micronutrients and make them unavailable to plants while concentrating harmful molecules in the soil
- Reduce soil fertility by attacking humus and organic matter reserves
- Increase salt concentration in the soil, changing the pH and adversely affecting plants
- Reduce the soil aggregation properties of microbes and sacrifice good tilth
- Effect is short-term. Requires frequent re-application.

FEED THE SOIL NOT THE PLANTS

Chemical fertilizer feeds only the plant, not the soil nor the microbes. Feeding chemicals to the plants instead of organics to the soil discards all the benefits from microbes. Organic matter feeds the beneficial microbes that make nutrients available for plants. When you feed the soil, you preserve the natural biological processes.

When you feed the soil, you preserve the natural biological processes

CHAPTER TWO

Understanding Plants

When you know how plants absorb nutrients from healthy soil, you become a better gardener. When you understand simple plant physiology, you see why plants respond as they do and how to grow them to their full potential.

Plants grow in proportion to the amount of light, water, minerals and oxygen they receive. Genes determine a plant's lifespan: one year for annuals, two for biennials and indefinitely for perennials. When a plant receives plenty of nutrients, careful watering, optimum sun energy for light and warmth, and thinning to remove competing plants, it can push to its limits of leaf and flower production.

For example, when you see the term *indeterminate* on tomato seed packets or seedling tags, it means the plant will continue to grow and bear fruit until environmental conditions, such as cold weather, stop the process.

Healthy plants strive to remain top competitors for their sustenance. Their well developed, more robust roots, stems and leaves naturally resist pests and diseases. If you minimize weeds (removing them by hand) your fruits and vegetables can compete against non-desirable plants. This helps ensure your plants absorb optimum nutrients.

Light, water, minerals and oxygen make plants grow

DEATH FEEDS NEW LIFE

At the end of their life cycle, healthy plants pass on essential nutrients to the next generation. After a plant dies, do not trash it. Instead, either compost it or turn it back into the soil. Microbes break down the dead plant into abundant nutrients

> Microbes break down dead plants into nutrients for the next crop

> Whatever you borrow from the soil, you must return

for the next crop. This positive loop can continue until your soil sustains healthy plant growth with little use of fertilizers.

At the beginning of the next crop cycle, you must replenish whatever the plants absorbed from the soil the previous growing seasons. Nutrients stored in soil are like a bank balance. When you withdraw from your account, your balance falls until you make a deposit to restore the original balance. Whatever you borrow from the soil, you must return to maintain the right balance for the next growing cycle.

WHAT PLANTS NEED:

The 16 Essential Nutrients
Crop development requires 16 basic nutrients (plus hundreds more they need in minute amounts. See below under Micronutrients.)

Plants absorb nutrients from soil, air and water. They use each mineral along with carbon and hydrogen to synthesize compounds such as phytonutrients, vitamins and anti-oxidants. They also help form compounds that provide structural support and transport nutrient-rich fluids throughout the plant.

While all plant nutrients are important, the right amount of each varies widely. These differences have led to grouping essential nutrients by the amount plants need. The large-quantity essentials are primary or macronutrients. Those in smaller amounts are secondary nutrients. The smallest, seen only at the microscopic level, are micronutrients.

You cannot know exactly how much of a nutrient a plant needs at a certain time of the year or hour of the day. Therefore, to get the best results, use long-lasting, ocean-based fertilizers. They safely ensure that all nutrients are available any time a plant needs them.

Macronutrients

The macronutrients, required in the largest amounts, are Nitrogen, Phosphorus and Potassium, or N-P-K, their chemical shorthand. Their absorption depends on the correct soil pH for your plants. Use the following descriptions as a reference.

NITROGEN (N) - Enables the plant to trap energy from sunlight via photosynthesis. Needed to produce amino acids, the building blocks for proteins and genetic material. Essential for plant cell division, vital for plant growth, a necessary component of vitamins, aids in production and use of carbohydrates and affects energy reactions in the plant.

Deficiency causes thin stems, yellow leaves, slowed growth and overall yellowing.

Excess causes an imbalance in metabolism. Flowering and fruiting can be delayed, with fruits ripening unevenly. Bud and blossom drop, low fruit production. Fruiting and flowering plants may not develop any fruits. May also inhibit the uptake of trace nutrients. Makes plants more susceptible to insects that feed on young, tender growth.

PHOSPHORUS (P) - Vital to seed formation. Needed for genetic material, cell membranes, root development, seed number and size. Involved in photosynthesis, respiration, energy storage and transfer, cell division and enlargement. Promotes early root formation and growth. Improves quality of fruits, vegetables and grains. Helps plants survive harsh winter conditions, increases water-use efficiency and hastens maturity.

Deficiency causes purple leaves beginning underneath, halted roots, slow growth, poor fruit and vegetable production. Excess toxicity is rare but possible if phosphorus fertilizer is over applied.

POTASSIUM (K) - Essential to protein synthesis. Important in fruit formation. Needed for carbohydrate metabolism, the break down and translocation of starches and cell division.

Long-lasting fertilizers from the ocean provide all nutrients safely

Influences the uptake of calcium, sodium and nitrogen. Increases photosynthesis and water-use efficiency. Activates enzymes and controls their reaction rates. Improves quality of seeds and fruit, improves winter hardiness, strengthens disease resistance.

Deficiency leads to flabby stems, halted growth, burnt leaf edges and vulnerability to disease.

Excess leads to deficiency in other nutrients. The plant will take up extra potassium before nutrients like magnesium.

Secondary Nutrients
The secondary nutrients are Calcium, Magnesium and Sulfur. Now that we know plants need more than N-P-K fertilizers to thrive, these play a larger role in fertilization programs.

CALCIUM (Ca) – Required for enzyme activation and cell re-production. Helps regulate access to plant cells similar to those needed for nitrogen uptake. Used for continuous cell division and formation. Involved in nitrogen metabolism. Reduces plant respiration, aids translocation of photosynthesis from leaves to fruiting organs, increases fruit set and stimulates microbial activity. Deficiency causes all growing tips to halt, curls leaves, and causes cell membranes to disintegrate, producing thin cell walls and blossom end rot.

MAGNESIUM (Mg) – Chlorophyll molecules need magnesium to make plants green. Also used for enzyme activation. Improves utilization and mobility of phosphorus. Increases iron utilization in plants and influences earliness and uniformity of maturity. Deficiency causes yellowing of lower leaves and, in some cases, lower crop yield.

SULFUR (S) – Integral to amino acids to build proteins. Contributes to the development of several enzymes and vitamins. Aids in seed production and promotes nodule formation on legumes. Needed in chlorophyll formation. Deficiency causes younger leaves to yellow.

MICRONUTRIENTS OR TRACE ELEMENTS

While plants use these in small amounts, they are equally as important as the macronutrients. Specifically, they activate or enable many plant functions, including chlorophyll formation, which affects photosynthesis. This is crucial for activating enzymes and forming hormones. They also aid vitamin formation, regulate metabolism and cell growth, promote the efficient use of nitrogen (thus protein formation) and enable photosynthesis.

If a plant is deficient in any of the essential micronutrients for a long period, noticeable symptoms develop. Depending on the plant species and the micronutrient, more or less than the right amount can cause major development problems or even death.

Sometimes deficiencies are not visible while they impede or block an internal plant process. For example, if a plant's cell walls are too thin, it becomes more susceptible to pests or disease. For this reason, you must learn how to interpret plant symptoms in order to know the right remedy. It often takes several years of growing experience, or a good mentor, to know how to diagnose and fix plant problems.

Micronutrients include Iron, Manganese, Zinc, Copper, Boron, Molybdenum and Chloride. Many others exist in the soil but are not fully understood. We know only that plants need them all in minute quantities. (You need proper pH here, too, for these nutrients to reach your plants.)

IRON (Fe) – Important for nitrogen fixation, chlorophyll synthesis and used in other enzymes and proteins.
Deficiency more likely in alkaline soil. Causes yellowing between enlarged veins and short, skinny stems.

MANGANESE (Mn) – Needed for synthesis of chlorophyll, assists in vitamin, carbohydrate and nitrogen metabolism.
Deficiency more likely in alkaline soil. Stops new leaf growth and pale color, mostly between veins.

Learn to interpret plant symptoms so you know the right remedy

ZINC (Z) – Needed to produce plant growth hormones. Essential to various enzyme systems for energy production, protein synthesis and growth regulation. Greatly benefits seed and grain production and maturation.

Deficiency displays yellowing and mottling of leaves. Plants also show delayed maturity. Not mobile in plants, so zinc deficiency symptoms occur mainly in new growth.

COPPER (Cu) – Important for reproductive growth. A catalyst for enzyme and chlorophyll synthesis. Aids root metabolism and helps in using proteins.

Deficiency symptoms generally appear on young plants. First symptoms are yellowing of youngest leaves with slightly stunted growth. In extreme cases, leaves die after becoming shriveled, twisted, broken and ragged.

BORON (B) – All growing tissues need. Exists in cell membranes. Needed for nitrogen fixation, protein synthesis, starch and sugar transport, root growth, water uptake and transport.

Deficiency more likely in alkaline soils. May lead to growing points dying and cells being disrupted.

MOLYBDENUM (Mo) – Important for nitrogen metabolism and protein synthesis. Needed to convert inorganic phosphates to organic forms.

Deficiency occurs mainly in acid soils. Can cause pale, deformed, thin leaves.

CHLORIDE (Cl) – Most soils have enough chloride for plant nutrition. Few areas are chloride deficient. This micronutrient is not considered in fertilizer programs.

Deficiency reported in sandy soils, in high rainfall areas or those derived from low-chloride parent materials.

Do not apply individual nutrients to the soil

To complete the list of 16 essential nutrients, plants also need Carbon, Hydrogen and Oxygen. They extract these elements from air and water to make up the bulk of their weight. They need them in only minute amounts to function properly.

Caution: Do not apply individual nutrients to the soil. An accidental overdose can be toxic or even fatal. You would need a laboratory analysis of the soil or leaf tissue to know which nutrient to add. Also, you would need a chemistry degree to be able to measure out the right amount of a specific nutrient.

Instead, take the easy way. Simply add and maintain natural and organic matter (seaweed, fish bone meal, rock powders) to insure adequate, balanced nutrition. As long as the soil has a balanced concentration of all nutrients, the plant's roots will absorb them in a continual process.

ADDING MICRONUTRIENTS

Soil can be depleted from over-gardening or farming. Micronutrient replenishment with organic fertilizers increases crop production and the nutrient value of fruits and vegetables. Amending the soil supports beneficial microbes and mycorrhizae, growing the bacteria needed for human and animal health.

Micronutrient-rich fertilizers can save you money, reduce fertilizer costs, save on energy use and decrease your carbon footprint. However, applying more does not always give more benefit. Getting the balance right is the key to success.

Get good information, not commercial advertising, for your plants' need for micronutrients. They are the soil catalysts that make other nutrients available.

Do not chase after easy, miracle results. The clever marketing of fertilizers urges you to apply only nitrogen, phosphorous and potassium. Do not be misled by photo ads that show beautiful, lush gardens fed by a hose-end sprayer with a simple, all-purpose blue fertilizer. This one-dimensional

Balance is the key to success

approach produces visible, short-term results and saves money, but it has long-term negative effects on the soil and overall plant health. The unbalanced approach of chemical N-P-K treatment eventually brings poor plant nutrition and lower yields.

UNDERSTAND YOUR SOIL

This is the time to study your soil, test it, track what you apply and consider buying a nutrient test kit and a pH meter. Know your soil's pH, since pH determines the availability of many nutrients. Using tests to measure the nutrients in your soil is always a good idea, but not always necessary if you are feeding with a complete fertilizer.

To get the best yields and optimum plant health, keep soil fertility in balance and do not cut back on nutrients. Field tests comparing simple N-P-K fertilizers with organic, blended fertilizers, show organic fertilizers give more micronutrients than N-P-K-only treatment.

ORGANIC SOURCES

The base ingredient of many organic fertilizers is usually one of the following:
• Chicken Manure or Dried Poultry Waste
• Kelp
• Feather Meal
• Blood Meal
• Soy Meal
• Cottonseed Meal
• Bone Meal
• Alfalfa Meal
• Fish Bone Meal
• Neem Meal

Chicken manure is fine but inferior. It decomposes too quickly and is like chemical fertilizers in its nearly water-soluble availability of nutrients. It is also very salty, which can upset the soil pH.

Other organic fertilizers use blood meal, bone meal or meat and bone meal as the base ingredient. These ingredients, too, are inferior and not to be trusted. Many experts report they can carry mad cow disease.

Organic fertilizers give more micro-nutrients than N-P-K

In general, do not use commodity meal ingredients. They are full of hormones and antibiotics given to caged chickens and feedlot animals that are fed GMO grains.

Be wise about your choices. Ask questions about the sources of chicken, blood and bone meal. Attend to these three in particular. While they are organic, they are not beneficial and safe. With soy and cottonseed meal, be sure they are free of GMOs.

OCEAN-RICH NUTRIENTS

Nutrients from the ocean are richest and safest. The ocean floor is the lowest spot on earth, where all nutrients eventually deposit. Micronutrients cycle back up the food chain and are absorbed by simple plankton and higher aquatic plants, which fish eat. Larger fish eat smaller fish, transferring the eroded micronutrients from microscopic elements to the larger fish we harvest from the ocean.

Fish is full of protein that breaks down and becomes a slow-release source of nitrogen. Kelp and seaweed contain amino acids, enzymes and carbohydrates, both simple and complex. Nutrient rich seaweeds and kelp meals contain important growth hormones that strengthen plant cell structure and vigor. They also enhance seed germination and increase the uptake of nutrients. Sea plants are full of micronutrients and potassium, an essential element for overall plant health and stress relief. Use ocean-based nutrients for complete plant nutrition.

Nutrients from the ocean are richest and safest

CHAPTER THREE

How to Make Your Garden Organic

All natural materials that contain carbon are organic

If you cannot quickly identify an ingredient on the label, don't use it

If you follow the soil amending guidelines in Chapter 2, you are well on your way to having an organic garden.

The term *organic* sometimes confuses people. To a chemist, organic means a carbon molecule is present. All natural materials that contain carbon are organic. Everything in your garden from a living source is organic.

Natural means something different and broader. Some of what is in your garden is natural but not organic. Sand, for example, comes from rocks ground to a fine texture. They do not come from a living source or have no carbon. Sand and stones are natural but not organic.

Organic when applied to gardening means something more complex than carbon. To deserve the label *organic*, your garden soil must have no synthetic pesticides, herbicides, fertilizers and genetically modified organisms (GMOs).

ORGANIC GARDENING vs. ORGANIC GROWING

In your backyard garden, you grow a small crop for your personal use. Whatever methods you use, you may call your garden organic. In your backyard or community plot, you may do anything you want to your plants. (You still may not contaminate the soil with toxic materials or pathogenic organisms.) You grow things, but you are not a grower. Organic growing produces food to sell. All organic produce grown and distributed in the U.S. must follow strict guidelines set by the USDA

(U.S. Department of Agriculture) or private certifying agencies like the C.C.O.F. (California Certified Organic Farmers) and OMRI (Organic Materials Review Institute.) The certifying agencies assure farmers do not use anything synthetic or unsafe for human exposure.

Growers who adhere to the above rules can be certified as organic. Certification matters to commercial growers who must prove they are growing by accepted standards in order to label their produce organic.

For you the home gardener, certified is a useless term. Certification should matter to you only when you go to a farmer's market or a grocery store to buy organic produce you cannot grow yourself.

WHAT IS ORGANIC PRODUCE?

Organic produce, regardless of its source, is grown according to the standards above: no use of or exposure to synthetic (non-organic or non-natural) herbicides, pesticides, fertilizers or GMOs.

NOT ALL ORGANIC IS GOOD

Caution: Do not uncritically accept everything labeled organic. Unless you know organic practices and techniques, you cannot know the effects your methods will have on plants, people or your environment. To be safe and successful as a gardener, you should understand how and why organic is good and when it is not.

For example, if too many microbes are applied in an organic fertilizer based on chicken manure, it acts like a synthetic fertilizer. The excess microbial action digests the organic fertilizer too quickly, making the soil lose nutrients before the plant roots can absorb them.

Best gardening advice: Read the labels and ask questions about the source of everything you apply to your soil and

When you hear or read *organic*, look for the certificate

Know how and why organic is good

plants. If you cannot quickly identify an ingredient on the label, don't use it.

THE ORGANIC GARDENER

While organic gardeners agree on avoiding synthetic pesticides, herbicides, fertilizers and GMOs, they otherwise follow a variety of gardening rules.

On the strict side, organic gardeners believe a plant should not receive any type of nutrient beyond what is native to the local area. A more liberal approach allows treating the soil, feeding the foliage, and introducing treatments that control temperature and light availability.

Regardless of approach, the organic gardener knows his local soil, plants and animals by getting close to the environment. He also needs to be inquisitive, practical, and attentive to detail. In his highest ideals, he cherishes the health and well being of his family, community and world.

WHY GO ORGANIC?

People give five main reasons to choose organic gardening.

- Better Tasting, Healthier Food: The best, most nutritious food is picked ripe and eaten fresh near where it grew in healthy soil.

- Safety: Organic methods reduce human exposure to potentially harmful chemicals, especially for infants and children. The increasing demand for organically grown produce shows people have a strong desire for healthy, safe food.

- Peace of Mind: You can be confident the food you grow is free of chemical residues and other pollutants from commercial farming. Also, organic methods do not lead to lower yields nor lower quality. With organics you may well increase both.

- Repairing the Earth: Organic methods cultivate the soil and modify it, leaving it better, more fertile than you found it. Organic gardening counters global warming by working organic materials back into the soil until microorganisms use it as an energy source. The energy then passes in diverse compounds for actively growing plants to use. When animals and humans consume these plants, carbon dioxide is sequestered that would otherwise release into the atmosphere. Even your small backyard garden makes a difference at the global level.

- Harmony with Nature: Sound organic methods safely mimic the life processes of the natural world, support habitat for wildlife and keep a balanced ecosystem.

THE ORGANIC WAY TO CONTROL PESTS AND DISEASE

Healthy plants naturally resist pest and diseases in two ways. First, the thicker a plant cell wall, the more it resists infection and insect attack. Second, a weak and susceptible plant transmits an electro-magnetic signal in a frequency range that destructive insects can detect, calling them to come and eat it. Healthy plants do not invite pests so easily.

Do not strive for perfection. Plants do not naturally grow to the beauty standards of perfection (no spots, smooth complexion) you see in a supermarket produce section. You can still have high yields and eat nutritious, healthy produce without pursuing the impossible goal of exterminating all pests, diseases and weeds.

You cannot conquer Nature. Instead, live in harmony with it. As an organic gardener, you can manage disease and pest problems in a way that is non-toxic, sustainable and gratifying.

Organically acceptable control methods have three characteristics that set them apart from synthetics:
- Derived from natural substances
- Less toxic to humans than synthetic pesticides
- Quickly break down to harmless substances

Organic
methods do
not lead to
lower yields

The organic approach uses strategies that blend with natural processes to control pests and disease. For example, if an insect lands on an organically treated tomato plant, the pungent odor of garlic extract and strong essential oils such as rosemary or clove will induce it to fly or crawl away from a plant it normally feeds on. Some of these natural insecticide components are made by grinding raw plant materials, such as flowers, roots, stems or seeds. Others are extracted from plant materials, then refined and purified into essential oils.

These highly specialized essential oil blends—in the proper ratios—kill insects, deter insect feeding, and confuse the pests' smell receptors (often located on their feet). Essential oils also make pest habitats inhospitable. They coat and suffocate insects, fungi and scales. Essential oils also reduce the number of pest eggs laid and the amount of feeding damage caused by a broad range of pests.

Most plant pathogens are fungal. If you limit or remove the environment that encourages fungus to grow, you minimize their ability to thrive and destroy your garden. For example, dark and damp soil under an overhead sprinkler system is the perfect environment for fungus.

By contrast, if the soil contains enough organisms that feed on fungus, many fungal spores will be eaten before they can grow and spread. Keep soil well-aerated and evenly moist to help control fungal pathogens and discourage harmful bacteria.

Fungi are some of the worst enemies in your garden. Pythium and rhizoctonia (damping-off), thielaniopsis (black root rot), and other root rot and wilt organisms such as fusarium and phytophthora, can quickly destroy an entire garden.

The safe, organic control method uses a natural process called general suppression. Healthy soil is full of beneficial bacteria such as Bacillus subtilis and Bacillus megaterium. Further, it has mycorrhizal fungi, which suppress fungal pathogens.

Use strategies that blend with natural processes

To make sure your soil is not deficient in any of these, you can apply naturally occurring antibiotic compounds, such as soil probiotics. These beneficial organisms are sold in various organic fertilizers, soils and soil inoculants that suppress pathogens through antagonism, competition, predation, and induced resistance.

Biodiversity is another key factor in organic control. The living variety of organisms in the soil, both micro and macro, helps regulate fungal pathogens and insects. Beneficial nematodes, mites, and mycorrhizal fungi also fight pest and disease problems.

Healthy soil is full of beneficial bacteria

TECHNIQUES TO MANAGE PESTS AND DISEASES

The first step is to grow strong and healthy plants in the best soil. Not all conditions warrant the use of insecticides or fungicides. Pests can become resistant to chemical treatment. Consider these alternatives.

Natural Chemical-Free Methods

Natural methods manage and prevent harm to plants by pests or diseases. The first step is to identify the disease or pest and when they are active. Then you can develop ways to minimize the damaging effects. Here are a few.

Remove pests by hand or rinsing. Some pests crawl along leaves, eating them or using them to lay their eggs. Catching and removing pests early, while requiring more labor, can prevent exponentially escalating problems.

Some pests, like slugs and snails, are more active on damp nights, while others are active during dry sunny days. Some pests can be rinsed off plants with a powerful stream of water. Attachments that hook up to your hose are designed to blast bugs off foliage.

Natural methods manage and prevent harm to plants

Removing pests by hand or rinsing is better than spraying, especially near ponds, streams or lakes, since pesticides can injure or kill aquatic life.

Remove badly infested or diseased plants to minimize spreading to healthy neighboring plants. Put infested or diseased plants in a closed plastic bag and remove them from your property to minimize contamination. Never dig anything diseased or infested back into your soil. Put it into a municipal green waste composting container, if possible. If nothing else, bag it and trash it.

Install barriers, which come in several different types. To protect smaller plants from birds or animals, build a small frame around the plant and enclose the area with mesh netting. You can also cover groups of fruits like apples or pears with pantyhose or tights to stop insects or birds from feeding on your freshly ripe fruit.

Place cut-off plastic bottles around smaller plants to help protect and warm up the soil around the roots. This promotes microbe activity.

Row covers made from material with small holes can protect entire rows from birds, beetles, bad worms and maggots. Cabbage maggots like to lay their eggs in the soil right around plants. You can deter them by placing a collar made of cardboard or other fabric around the stems. This causes females to lay their eggs on the collar where the eggs will dry out before hatching.

Pheromones are gaseous chemicals that insects and animals use to communicate, locate plants or find a mate. A trap can attract pests so you can monitor when they are active and most destructive. You can then determine the best time to apply a pesticide or other method to stop the offspring from causing plant damage.

Sticky traps used in various locations can stop pests cold. Non-flying insects travel up and down plants such as trees. Placing a sticky band around, but not touching, the tree trunk will deter pests from reaching the fruit. You can also place other sticky bands around containers to stop bugs like ants or earwigs. Traps can be hung above plants in greenhouses

Never dig anything diseased or infested back into your soil

to capture flying pests. This step indicates the extent of the invasion. Additional controls may further deter plant damage.

Other traps such as half-full cans of beer, can be buried at soil level near plants to attract slugs and snails. They fall in, get drunk and drown.

Repellents usually deter birds, deer, rodents and moles by using bothersome smells, tastes or noises these animals do not tolerate. Soaps, oils and noise repellents are available at some nurseries. For getting rid of moles or gophers, try this trick. At your local barbershop, ask for some cut hair they normally sweep up and discard. Place the hair in the rodent's hole. Gophers and moles will sense a human is down there with them and avoid your garden. Buried hair also breaks down into nitrogen-rich fertilizer.

Biological Pest Control Tactics

Here you recruit the help of pest predators or spraying pests with living organisms. Remember the checks and balances of biodiversity. But if the balance is off, you can use these techniques.

> Repellents use smells, tastes or noises that animals avoid

Releasing pest predators like ladybugs and praying mantis are a good, safe approach. Planting flowers and other shrubs around the garden can attract and provide shelter for pest eaters such as birds, frogs, toads, bats and certain insects. This is called companion planting.

A small body of water nearby, such as a pond, provides a breeding ground for creatures like frogs and toads. If you add pest predators, avoid following it with an insecticide, which can kill off the predators and be a waste of money. If you must spray, do it first, and release predators a few days later.

Beneficial microbes – Bt, or Bacillus thuringiensis – can safely control lepidopteron larvae (caterpillars.) This is one of the most effective ways to get rid of leaf-chewing pests. Different treatments operate best under certain environmental conditions. For instance, Bt is less effective when applied in direct sun. Caterpillars feed only in warm weather, so apply Bt when it is warm, but not in direct sun, to maximize its potential. Early morning is the best time to apply.

Botanical sprays use essential oils like cinnamon, clove, mint, rosemary, eucalyptus and wintergreen oil to kill and control a wide variety of pests by immobilizing them. These substances kill by blocking chemical signals that control body functions. Botanical oils are completely derived from plants. They quickly break down to harmless substances that do not damage the environmental.

Garlic extract also repels pests. Most pests have their smell receptors on the bottom of their legs. When they land on a plant that has been sprayed with essential oils or garlic, they detect an aroma different from their target plant and move on to neighboring plants.

Chemical Approaches

Use these as a last resort when nothing else has worked. If you have a biologically diverse garden, you may never need a toxic chemical to control pests or disease. However, if you do use chemicals, read the label carefully and never over apply. More is not better.

Remember that insects develop resistance to pesticides, requiring stronger and more frequent applications to be effective. Toxic pesticide use may be detrimental to the environment and severely disrupt the balance of living organisms in the soil.

Pesticides are also severe pollutants of ground water, lakes, rivers and oceans. While more detrimental on the large-scale farm, using synthetic pesticides in your backyard also damages the environment. Consider using a chemical only when nothing else will work to save your crop.

TO SPRAY OR NOT TO SPRAY

Unfortunately, in some cases you don't have a choice between using chemical treatments and letting Nature take its course. When an infestation grows out of control, the only quick way to get rid of pests may be to use an extermination spray. Fortunately, some well-developed treatments have minimal side effects when used properly.

Pay close attention to the plant toxicity of each method to avoid killing the plants you want to salvage. Never spray a plant with any treatment in direct sunlight. Even the safest of treatments can be harmful if applied in direct sunlight.

Treating plants is sometimes like treating people. You can treat the symptoms or think more deeply about the cause of a disease. The same symptom and disease relationship holds true for plants. If the soil is healthy and full of biodiversity, you can prevent disease instead of treating symptoms.

CHAPTER FOUR

Healthy Diet, Healthy You

ORGANIC EATING

Often the best advice is simple. Choose a wide variety of healthful foods grown in natural soil. Cook them as little as you need to make them appealing and digestible.

This way of eating goes by many names. Whatever the name, these are a few simple guidelines.

- Eat whole foods in their natural form. The less you do to a food, the more nutrients it retains.
- Eat food grown organically. No chemicals in or on the produce. No antibiotics or growth hormones in the meat and poultry. (Shop at a farmer's market or look for produce certified as organic. Buy grass-fed beef and free-range chicken from a butcher you trust.) Prefer fatty fish caught wild not farmed.
- Avoid processed, refined, nutrient-poor foods, including grains, legumes, processed oils and refined sugar in its many disguises. Eat nothing from a "food factory" or with a long list of unfamiliar ingredients.

START SMALL IF YOU MUST

If you cannot go completely organic at first, you can still get many nutritional benefits from organic food without straining your food budget. First, buy those organic foods that have more nutritional value than conventional produce:

- Lettuce
- Cabbage
- Potatoes
- Spinach
- Carrots

Buy those organic foods that have more nutritional value

Other studies show that milk, oranges, peaches and other fruits have more nutrition in their organic versions.

Second, limit your toxic exposure by buying the organic versions of those foods most heavily sprayed with pesticides. The Environmental Working Group has developed a list of 12 fruits sprayed most heavily with pesticides.

- Apples
- Celery
- Nectarines
- Pears
- Raspberries
- Strawberries
- Bell peppers
- Cherries
- Peaches
- Potatoes
- Spinach
- Grapes (especially imported)

The 12 foods below are the least tainted by pesticide residues. If you have to buy conventionally grown produce, start with these without much concern.

- Asparagus
- Bananas
- Cauliflower
- Kiwi
- Onions
- Pineapples
- Avocados
- Broccoli
- Sweet corn
- Mangoes
- Papaya
- Sweet peas

> Buy the organic versions of foods most-heavily sprayed with pesticides

HOW RAW ORGANIC FOOD MAKES THE DIFFERENCE

Organic food is healthier for you in two ways: nutrient density and purity. Whole, natural foods give you bioavailable nutrients. Because these foods are at or close to their natural state, they easily break down for maximum use. The simpler the molecule, the easier it is for you to absorb.

Bioavailability varies among people because we are unique individuals. The important variables include how foods are cooked, how fast a person chews and swallows, enzymes and probiotics in the digestive tract, age, alcohol consumption, metabolic rate, gastrointestinal disorders or disease, and general health.

Also, when you eat organic food, you avoid or stop exposing yourself to the wide array of pesticides, heavy metals, nitrates and other contaminants in conventional crops. Minimizing contamination and bioaccumulation helps you get closer to the best health you can achieve. Finally, if you want to get or keep your healthy weight, organic produce lets you eat less, because the nutrient density is higher.

NUTRIENTS AND YOUR HEALTH

Organic crops contain significantly more phytonutrients than conventionally grown foods. Acting as nutraceuticals, phytonutrients support healthy blood vessels, connective tissue, major organs and all other parts of the body. They protect us from toxics in the environment and in conventionally grown food. They also help control different bacteria and pathogenic fungi, free radicals and carcinogens. Phytonutrients come in all colors including green, yellow, red and purple. Grow a wide color variety of fruits and vegetables to gain a wider spectrum of phytonutrients.

ANTIOXIDANTS AND DISEASE PREVENTION

Organic produce also offers many antioxidants (vitamin C, polyphenols and flavonoids), micronutrients and minerals. The word *antioxidant* literally means "against oxidation."

Antioxidant is a collective term for micronutrients, trace elements, vitamins, polyphenols, and carotenoids. Antioxidants protect you against the damaging effects of free radicals, some of which come from environmental exposures to air and water pollution, radiation, herbicides and cigarette smoke.

Antioxidants can even affect genetic makeup, the DNA that carries your genetic code and helps determine your lifespan. For example, the extra-long lifespan of the Japanese is partly due to their diet of raw vegetables and fish, both rich in antioxidants.

The most common antioxidant foods include liver, fish, grains, nuts, citrus, berries, tomatoes, colored fruits, and vegetables.

Grow a wide color variety of fruits and vegetables

One of the protective antioxidants is sulforaphane, found in cruciferous vegetables such as kale and broccoli. (They are called cruciferous because of the cross-like shape of their cell arrangement.) In studies of rats and mice, sulforaphane inhibited the development of cancer in many organs. Human studies have yet to find a strong link to reduced risk of cancer, but cruciferous vegetables do inhibit the carcinogenic process. They also support all the organs that detoxify the bloodstream and increase the bioavailability of other nutrients.

Why care about oxidation and the damaging effects of free radicals? Oxidation breaks down the body at the cellular level. Free radicals rob electrons from molecules and the cell membranes that encompass the DNA in your genes. As the molecules react with each other, free radicals damage the connective tissue of muscles, organs and other complex structures. Free radicals can also cause cognitive impairment, macular degeneration, cataracts, Alzheimer's disease, immune dysfunction, cardiovascular diseases and a variety of cancers.

Antioxidants stop this destructive process by neutralizing free radicals. The human body does eventually break down, but antioxidants help keep it together longer.

PREBIOTICS AND HIGH-FIBER FOODS

Prebiotics are non-digestible, high-fiber ingredients that form a receptive environment for the beneficial probiotics in your intestines. Typically, they are carbohydrates found in grains and greens, but they can also come from soluble fibers. Fruits and vegetables, especially fibrous ones with thick veins, also promote healthy bowel regularity.

The digestive tract slows down on a diet of meats and highly processed foods loaded with simple sugars and preservatives. Metabolism (the rate at which you burn calories for energy) also slows. When digestion and elimination are sluggish, the colon fills with undigested, putrefied waste. The longer this toxic matter sits in your intestines, the greater the risk it will leak into your system with potentially devastating results. The high-fiber foods (fruits, vegetables and whole grains) along with probiotics help your body quickly remove waste and non-essentials. These healthy foods literally drag out impurities through elimination.

HEALTHY DIET

Eat from your garden what is good for your health. (See the 100 Plants section for details on what to plant, how to grow it and the health benefits.)

For most people, the ideal diet includes a wide variety of fresh fruits and vegetables, plus protein from simple, healthy sources. You don't have to eat meat to be healthy. Plenty of lifelong vegetarians have all the nutrition they need to remain healthy and vigorous. To eat meat or not is a lifestyle choice based on personal values.

Whatever lifestyle choices you make, eating plenty of fruits and vegetables takes the guesswork out of finding nutrient balance. Mother Nature is the best chemist. Raw or lightly cooked foods give the best bioavailability, which is the ratio of how much of a nutrient you eat to how much of it you absorb. Only what you can absorb nourishes you.

SUPPLEMENTS

If you take vitamin and mineral supplements, make sure they are food-based. Complement supplements with synergistic, broad-spectrum catalysts such as probiotics and a wide variety of digestive enzymes. These will help your body extract the nutrients in food to make them bioavailable.

WHERE TO SHOP

The Farmer's Market First

The healthiest food you can buy is grown by certified organic farmers near you. These devoted men and women are close to the earth and have chosen to help feed people the healthy,

Eating fruits and vegetables takes the guesswork out of nutrient balance natural way. They deserve your support and encouragement for many reasons.

Visiting a farmer's market is like a large community gathering. You get to know and trust the farmers you see again and again, as well as your like-minded neighbors.

What you spend at the farmer's market supports your local economy not a distant mega-corporation.

For many people, the farmer's market is part of their regular schedule. They don't want to miss it.

THE BEST PRODUCE YOU CAN BUY
The produce at a farmer's market is:
- Safe (no pesticides or other chemicals)
- Healthy (higher nutrient density)
- Fresh (never frozen or gassed)
- Tasty
- In Season
- Diverse (varieties you can't find in supermarkets)
- Local (not trucked or flown from far away)

Once you find a farmer's market you like, you may never want to go back to a supermarket. (Note: Not everything at a farmer's market will be organic. Look for the organic certificate on the booth. Or ask. Some farmers are on their way to becoming organic. Talk with them about their methods. Some foods that don't meet strict organic rules are still nutritious and healthy for you.)

WHAT TO AVOID
Your local supermarket is not a healthy place to buy your food. Except for the organics you can trust, little in a conventional grocery store has good nutrition and taste. Processed and packaged food (with the nutrition diminished) is full of chemical preservatives that give it shelf life but no positive nutrition. It uses salt as a preservative and sugar and fats to make it taste good. Your taste buds are not educated in nutrition.

Even grocery store produce is not safe or healthy. Most of the fruits and vegetables have been grown in dead soil, exposed to chemical fertilizers, herbicides and pesticides. They are also picked before they are ripe, exposed to gases to accelerate the ripening, refrigerated to retard spoilage, and trucked hundreds of miles to the store. For stores in the Northern Hemisphere, out-of-season fruits, such as apples and grapes, can be flown thousands of miles from New Zealand and Chile.

What the grocery store offers you was not grown or made with your health in mind. What then? Corporate profits.

In one sense, your local supermarket is not really a local business. It is a distribution point at the end of a huge, profit-driven system to produce cheap, "food-like" substances for a population that cannot tell the difference between a real tomato and one from a food factory. Grocery store produce often is low in taste and nourishment but profitable.

Taste and freshness aside, the imitation tomato has little food value. Low-quality produce has low amounts of total dissolved sugars and low nutrient content. Your body needs to convert dissolved sugars into the energy you need for life. You get that from sweet, juicy produce picked ripe.

Beyond the produce section, almost everything the supermarket sells has been highly processed and carefully packaged to make you want it while you ignore what is in it. Food processors use an array of synthesized chemicals to fabricate the taste, texture and appearance of what you eat. Food additives are not there for your nutrition but to make the pseudo food a more profitable product.

Supermarket food undermines your health by exposing you to chemicals and other substances linked to the diseases of modern society: cancer, heart disease, diabetes, stroke and obesity. These all stem from or are made worse by how we live, what we eat and the environment we live in. The "grocery store diet" is not healthy for you.

> Little in a conventional grocery store has good nutrition and taste

BE FLEXIBLE AND MODERATE

Not everyone has the time or energy to shop organically. If you work a 9-to-5 job (or longer) and live in a small rented space in the middle of the city, growing your own food can seem like a fantasy. Yet, some people make a small vertical garden on a sunny balcony. You can grow something to enjoy even in that tiny space such as herbs or the vine climbing varieties of beans and peas.

For most people, shopping at the supermarket is practical and a strong habit. It's convenient to where they live or work. They know what to expect and are lured in by weekly specials. And the food is consistent from month to month. Plus, the supermarket often has a pharmacy and a liquor department attached. Most people cannot resist all that convenience and security.

Even if you shop regularly at a supermarket, you can still support organic values and ideals. When you buy organic food in your local market, you help support the farmers who made the expensive and difficult conversion from conventional to organic methods. While organic food costs more than conventional food, you have to measure the short-term cost against the long-term benefit of conserving our soil and eating produce that supports your overall good health.

Converting a farm from conventional to organic methods requires an enormous investment risk in both money and time. You can support and motivate the people making these conversions by buying as much organic food as you can afford from local markets. By the sources you choose to obtain your food, you vote for how you want your food produced.

Growing and eating organically is a lifestyle and life-changing decision. As you ask questions and learn more, one day going organic will seem like a small step toward a better, healthier life.

> You can make a small, vertical garden on a sunny balcony

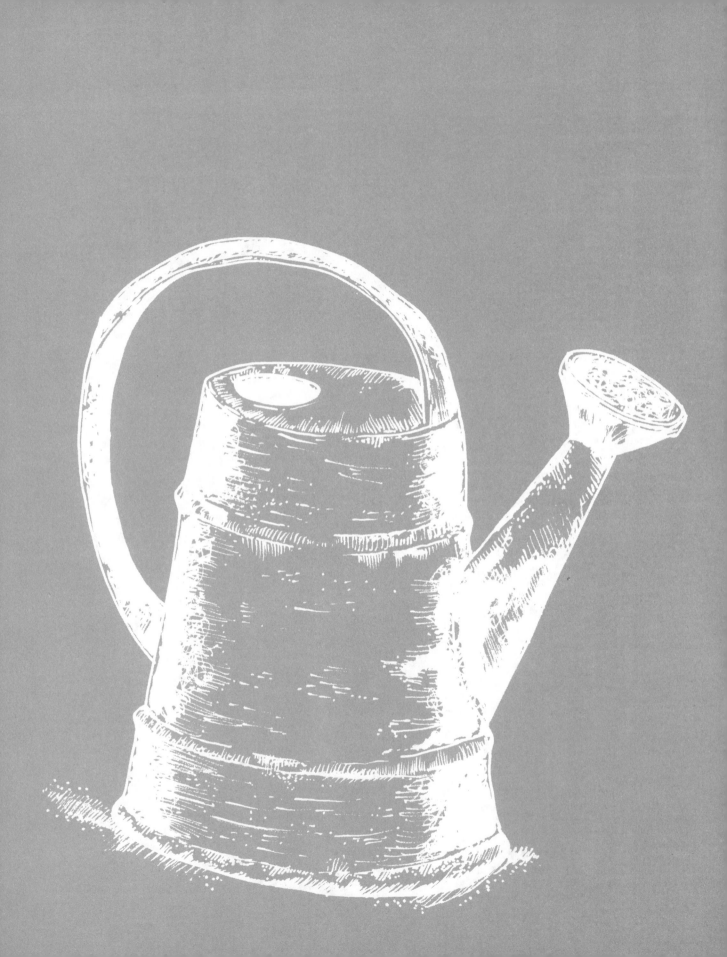

CHAPTER FIVE

Gardening Basics

Gardening is a huge subject. The *California Master Gardener's Handbook* is 700 pages long and 1.75 inches thick. It tells you nearly everything you need to know except the latest research results and prices. And there is always more to know.

To get started as a new gardener, you need to consider only a few basic matters. This brief primer touches lightly on them so you know what to expect and how to make choices that are right for you.

BASIC FACTORS
- Plant Zone
- Environment/Microclimate
- Sunlight
- Soil
- Drainage
- Fertilizer
- Water

PLANT ZONE/HARDINESS ZONE
Learn the usual dates of your first frost and the springtime thaw. These dates determine the beginning and end of your growing season and what you can plant and grow.

The USDA publishes a hardiness zone map, which divides the continental U.S. into 11 zones. These are based on the average annual low temperature, from zone 1 (-50° F, long hard freezes) to zone 11 (+40°F long, hot summers). The maps are online or in most gardening manuals. Or ask at your local nursery.

If you buy seeds and plants from catalogues, invest in a *Sunset* reference book. Besides the climate zones, these books completely describe every plant appropriate for your region. With many color photographs, these are fun to browse for ideas and inspiration.

Or just visit a local nursery. Anything you see there will surely grow in your backyard. Their business depends on selling what grows well for their customers.

Pay attention to your weather patterns both annual and seasonal. A comprehensive weather report (rain, wind, high and low pressure and temperature extremes) helps you plan your activities. Note when seeds germinate and when insects begin to appear and which ones.

Know where the sun rises and sets in relation to your planting beds. They should run North-South for maximum sun exposure.

Invest in a good soil and air thermometer with high and low capabilities. It simplifies your life and helps you live with the elements.

Keep a journal of what you did, when, with what (including its source) and why. Unless you know what you began with, you cannot understand the lessons in your results. Gardening is often like doing a good science experiment. Keep good records and change only one thing at a time to get results you can use to make the right choices. As time and seasons go by, review your journal to help you decide what to do next time, perhaps even better.

> Keep good records and change only one thing at a time

MICROCLIMATES

Your garden may have one or more microclimates, pockets with warmer or cooler temperatures. These come in four types:
- a hot side facing South
- a shadowed, cool side facing North

- a warm side with afternoon sun facing West
- a variable side facing East

Carefully observe the heat and light. Hot and cold pockets can interfere with the plants you want. These areas will change daily and evolve as the seasons change. Anticipate these fluctuations as you plan your garden. For example, in winter, keep tall trellised plants against the north wall and the shorter plants to the south. In the summer, do the opposite.

SUNLIGHT AND SHADE

Plants that produce fruit must have direct sunlight. The larger the fruit, the more sunlight it needs. These need 6 hours daily:

tomatoes	cucumbers	cabbage
zucchini	peppers	beans
corn	eggplant	summer squash

You can grow in the shade, too. Leafy green vegetables and herbs do well with about four hours of daily sun:

carrots	beets	chard
cauliflower	chives	lettuce
chicories	radicchio	arugula
basil	mint	parsley
spinach	winter squash	

To measure your sunlight, track the sun and shade pattern. Here's an easy way: Pick a day during your growing season when you can check the sunlight often from early morning through late afternoon. Take any 6-hour period, say, 9-3 or 11-5. Note the areas that stayed sunlit. Those are your best growing areas.

DRAINAGE

Your plants and soil want water but not too much. They need to retain moisture but also to have air around their roots to drain away any excess. If you have a good balance among sand, silt, clay and organic materials, you have a solid foundation for good drainage.

The larger the fruit, the more sunlight it needs

A quick drainage test: Dig a hole about 1 foot deep and 6 inches wide. Fill the hole with water and let it drain completely. When the hole is empty, fill it again with water to the top. If it takes more than 10 hours to empty again, you have a drainage problem.

You can improve your drainage by adding organic materials. You can also add drainage pipes to direct the water away. Ask a landscape professional about the best solution for your garden.

RAISED BEDS ELEVATE YOUR GROWTH

You can avoid many problems by growing your crops in raised beds. The advantages are many:

- Total control over soil composition (fewer weeds and pathogens, correct pH and beneficial organisms)
- Soil is light, roots spread well because you do not walk on it.
- Higher crop yields (up to 40 percent more than direct planting)
- Easier to work in for planting and harvesting (less back strain)
- Better drainage
- Beautiful, depending on materials and design

You have many choices of materials for your raised bed:

- Brick and mortar
- Natural stone and mortar
- Hay bales
- Redwood or other untreated hardwoods

Avoid any pressure treated or painted wood. As they decompose, the chemicals contaminate the soil. Do not use cheap plastic beds. They look temporary and amateurish. Unless you live on the go, construct a real bed built to last.
After you build the beds, start on projects one bed at a time. Focus on one area every day or weekend so you are not overwhelmed by the entire garden.

Growing in raised beds has many advantages

CONTAINER GARDENING

Use containers to grow a small crop in a small space. If you give the plants what they need, you can grow organic food on a 4-foot by 8-foot balcony or even smaller space.

Consider five factors for a productive container garden:
- Sunlight
- Container size
- Potting medium
- Fertilizer
- Trellising support

SUNLIGHT

Sunlight is the most important factor to consider. See above.

CONTAINER SIZE

More soil equals more nutrition, because the larger root system can draw more nutrients via the water. Container space directly affects the nutrient value, size and quality of your harvest.

For example, tomatoes require a minimum of 15 gallons of soil to develop into full size plants with good taste and nutrition. Other vegetable crops can survive in smaller containers with less soil volume, but they still gain from more soil by producing larger, more bountiful crops in the larger container.

Terracotta containers breathe with the soil and do not fluctuate quickly with extreme temperatures. Redwood also breathes and retains moisture well. Plastic containers in a variety of styles work fine but need more watering than thicker, denser pots. With plastic containers, you must use mulch to retain moisture.

Remember water. Plants in small containers dry out quickly. Less plant foliage needs less regular watering; larger plants need more water. Pay close attention to your plants, and water regularly as they need.

Plants in small containers dry out quickly

POTTING MEDIUM

Healthy soil produces a healthy crop. The type of soil or potting medium you choose has a large effect on your plants and their ability to produce abundant, nutritious food.

Potting soil is different from composts or planting mixes. It can be difficult to formulate in order to get the balance right. You want potting soil to drain fast to prevent root rot. But you also need the soil to hold enough moisture to support a healthy transfer of nutrients to the roots.

A good component to mix with potting soil is the wet organic compost from your kitchen. A good formula is 2 to 1 potting soil to compost.

Do not skimp on the soil, as it is the only source of nutrition for your edibles. Spend a few extra dollars for the best soil you can get. Container plants cannot draw nutrients from the native soil but only from what you give them. Find a potting mixture that gives you good results, and stay with it. Watch out for synthetic plant nutrients in many bagged potting soils. Make sure your bagged potting medium has no chemicals.

FERTILIZER

You must feed the soil that feeds your plants' root systems. Fruit trees, tomatoes and most other vegetables, especially in containers, need a lot of fertilizer to reach full potential. The plants receive only what you give them in the container. Feed the roots slowly with the best quality organic fertilizer.

Sea-based organic fertilizers are superior and contain the most multi-minerals.

Feed containers every two months to maximize plant potential. In a confined space, it will quickly use all the nutrients. Keep container plants on a regular feeding schedule.

Spend a few extra dollars for the best soil

TRELLISING SUPPORT

Cucumbers, tomatoes and other vine plants need support to keep them off the ground and growing where you want them. Exposing as many leaves to sunlight as possible helps to increase your harvest.

Air space between your plants is also important to help minimize fungal diseases. Air space also encourages beneficial insects to do their pollination work more easily by making flowers more accessible.

When you buy trees or vegetable transplants, ask a nursery professional about support. Some plants need a stake in the center of the container. A tomato wants a sturdy cage. A cucumber needs a grid-like trellis. You can build many of these support systems from scraps around the house. Whatever you ·use, the plants do not know the difference. Just give them a shoulder to lean on!

WATERING

When and how often to water depends on your unique garden. No fixed watering schedule can be prescribed. Pay attention to soil, weather, dryness and humidity. You must base your watering decisions on observation not rigid rules.

Water when it feels right to you. Probe your finger 1-2 inches into the soil to feel if it is dry or moist. You can buy a water meter at your local nursery, but you get closer to your garden when you touch the soil with your bare hands.

Water in early to mid-morning to reduce evaporation and avoid frying plant foliage. This gives your plants the entire day to draw water from the soil as needed, especially on hot days. This also allows foliage to dry off to reduce the risk of disease. Water slowly to insure proper absorption and deeply to reach the root zone. Avoid getting the soil waterlogged, which also invites disease.

Pay attention to shady spots. They need less water, while the

> Base your watering decisions on observation not rules

sunny areas dry out more quickly.

GARDEN PLAN

A happy garden has a plan so that it all works together. You can find sample garden plans with explanations online and in many books. Among many questions to answer:

- What is the nutrient value of a desired plant?
- How hardy are the plants you want to grow?
- What are the sun requirements for your plants?
- What is the best soil mixture for you?
- Will you plant in the ground or use raised beds?
- Water: sprinkler system, hand irrigation or drip irrigation?
- Will you start from seeds or transplants?
- How will the elements of your garden work together?
- Where will the same plant go next year?
- What plants are you going to grow in summer, winter or fall?.
- Keep looking for answers. You can never know too much about your garden and your health.

A FEW OTHER TIPS

Weeding reduces the competition for nutrients in the soil. Remove weeds as quickly as possible before they produce seeds. Weeds also attract pests and diseases.

Remove dead, diseased or damaged parts of plants immediately to avoid compromising the rest of the plant.

Prune woody plants by making cuts just beyond a bud and slightly angled to promote bud growth. Cuts at too sharp an angle or below a bud prevent bud growth. If cutting an entire branch, leave a small portion attached to the trunk to avoid exposing bare wood.

Crop rotation breaks pest and disease life cycles, reduces weed invasion and restores depleted nutrients.

Rotate plants from the same family every 2 to 3 seasons to avoid depleting essential nutrients. Make a number of beds equal to the number of plant families you grow. If you re-amend the soil before each growing season, this is less of a problem but is still good practice.

BEYOND THE BASICS
For more information and guidance, look for:
- an organic gardening manual
- a seasoned gardener
- staff at a good independent nursery
- a local garden club
- online sites of all kinds and qualities

Caution: Gardening is based on good science. Learn to tell a fact (which can be verified) from an opinion (which is based on information filtered through values and personal observation.) Learn to tell the difference between one person's success story, supported by believers, and a proven method based on many careful repetitions by people you trust.

When you choose among sources of information, watch out for your own biases. We tend to listen to and follow people we agree with who tell us what we want to hear. Choose a diversity of sources for balance.

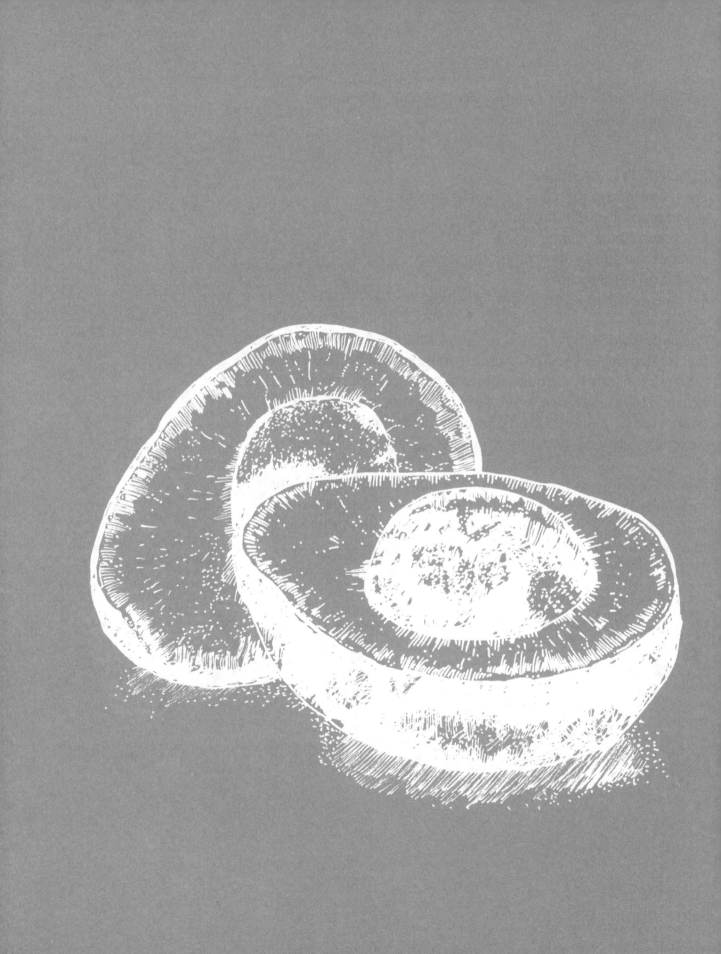

CHAPTER SIX

100 Plants to Grow and Eat for Your Health

The list covers the top 100 fruits, vegetables and herbs you can grow and eat for your wellbeing. Each listing begins with the nutritional value of the plant, its health power and disease prevention qualities, as far as we know them. The next part tells the practical details of how to grow it in your garden.

The plants are in alphabetical order by their common names. They meet three criteria:
- Important nutritional value
- Easy to grow in most regions
- Easy to find at your local nursery

You can easily remember and give the common name to the local nursery or farmers market seller to grow or buy that plant with ease and no further reference. You might call this "gardening for the rest of us."

The list includes some warm climate plants, such as citrus and avocados. These may not be practical in Michigan or Minnesota unless you build a greenhouse. Still, you can gain from knowing the nutritional quality and importance of a plant, even if you do not grow it, because you can buy and eat its organic version.

Your garden can give you healthy food

Alfalfa Sprouts

HEALTH POWER

Health benefits come from phytonutrients not vitamins and minerals, which are in trace amounts except for vitamin K. Nutrient quantity low if eating only a few sprouts in salads or sandwiches. More concentrated dose comes from juicing. Phytonutrients include an amino acid derivative, canavanine, plant estrogens and saponins. Early studies of canavanine suggest it may help fight leukemia and cancers of the colon and pancreas. Abundant plant estrogens may support bone formation and inhibit deterioration. May also protect against many cancers (ex. breast, bowel and prostate). Saponins lower bad cholesterol (LDL) and help stimulate parts of immune system.

VITAMIN & MINERAL

Vitamins – K, C and traces
Minerals – Copper, Manganese and traces

DISEASE PREVENTION

Sprouts or juice may help prevent or reduce symptoms of osteoporosis, atherosclerosis, cardiovascular disease and many cancers.

HOW TO GROW

A perennial legume requiring soil with good drainage and pH near 6.5. Can be used as green manure and added to soil as nitrogen-rich organic matter. Many farmers plant these cover crops after fall harvest, let grow over winter and till in spring. Excellent way to maintain soil tilth, organic matter and nutrient content. Other gardeners or farmers work alfalfa into crop rotation plan to help restore soil fertility during part of year. Sow in spring. Till into soil in fall. In warmer climates, sow in fall and till in spring. Sowing for food is fun project. Use sterile, clear, quart glass jar, seeds, cheesecloth or other filter material with small pores for draining, rubber band and windowsill or sunny indoor location. Put tablespoon of seeds in glass jar. Cover seeds with lukewarm filtered water to 1-2 inches above seeds. Secure filter material (cheese cloth or pantyhose) around top with rubber band. Let seeds soak overnight. Drain jar the next day by inverting over sink, leaving only enough moisture to keep seeds damp. They grow best in 70-80°F. Place jar in the dark undisturbed for four days. Each day, remove seeds and rinse with quality water up to three times a day. Drain out so seeds are damp but not soaked. Watch seeds turn white and grow several inches over a few days. After rinsing and draining on day 4, place sprouts on a tray on windowsill or sunny spot. In 15 minutes they turn green and are ready to eat.

INSECT CONTROL	✗	Jar is protected from pests, which are not usually a problem.
TIPS	✓	For continual supply of sprouts, start a new jar every few days. Phyto-nutrient content of sprouts is highest after setting them in the sun and letting leaves turn green.

Almonds

HEALTH POWER	+	Health Power: Surprising benefit: high fat nut reduces risk of heart disease. Antioxidant Vitamin E, monounsaturated fats, fibers, other phyto-nutrients together reduce LDL blood cholesterol. Moderate eating (2-3 servings weekly) may help control weight. Also rich in magnesium (improves blood flow) and potassium (needed for neural firing and muscle contraction). When salt is absent, monounsaturated fats, magnesium and potassium prevent arterial plaque buildup, control blood pressure and improve heart performance. Several ounces reduce blood sugar, reducing demand on insulin-producing cells in pancreas. Also provide energy, help prevent gallstones and supply protein for building body structures. Almond skins give flavonoids with Vitamin E to enhance antioxidant action. Like all nuts, especially walnuts, promote good health. Eat a handful a day.
VITAMIN & MINERAL	↑	Vitamins - E, B2 (Riboflavin) Minerals – Manganese, Magnesium, Copper and Phosphorus
DISEASE PREVENTION	⊘	Lowers risk of cardiovascular disease, gall bladder disease and diabetes.
HOW TO GROW	༄	Grow similar to peaches. Tree spreads 20-30 feet. Dwarf variety spreads half that size. Choose among several cultivars. Consult nursery for which grows best in your location. Most popular is full-size, "all-in-one" cultivar: self-pollinating, high yielding, great tasting. Most popular dwarf is "Garden Prince" cultivar: self-pollinating and small enough to grow in containers. All produce delightful flowers in bloom. Best time to plant

is early in year when cooler temperatures prevent leaf growth and tree puts most of its energy into root expansion. Requires lighter loam, nutrient-rich soil with great drainage. Choose plot with full sunlight, few or no late-spring frosts, soil pH 6-6.5. Dig hole deep enough for taproot to fit undisturbed. Soften soil around the hole if needed to give roots pathways to grow and correct drainage issues. Carefully place tree in hole to avoid root damage. Fill with soil dug out while mixing in handfuls of organic matter (planting mix, compost or well-aged manure). Don't add too much or roots will remain in hole, making tree top heavy and vulnerable to blowing down. Mulch a few inches of compost or other material containing humus around the tree (not flush with base). Consider staking first year if tree grows tall before trunk thickens, especially if prevailing winds get strong. Water regularly first year to keep soil moist but not water logged. In dry, warm weather water longer to reach deeper soil. Ready for harvest after fruit surrounding almond, called drupe, dries out and cracks, revealing almond seed inside. Refer to Peaches for pruning after season ends. Three years needed for almond production but can continue for 50 years!

INSECT CONTROL ✕ Many different pests affect nut trees, none lethal. Encourage resilience by cultivating healthiest possible tree. Control leaf-eating caterpillars by hand or use Bt if needed.

TIPS ✓ Look to buy tree with straight trunk and slight widening at base. Look for branches well gapped and evenly spaced throughout trunk. When choosing where to grow, avoid location that has history of standing water. During flowering, do not water branches, which interferes with pollination and risks disease.

Aloe Vera

HEALTH POWER ✚ Used for centuries as a medical treatment. Juice from broken leaves soothes wounds, rejuvenates burns and treats rare skin conditions. Benefits of drinking juice less well known. Great for digestive tract. Helps maintain healthy tissues and promotes slower, more controlled absorption of food. Good source of essential amino acids that help replenish and build enzymes crucial to functions throughout the body. High volume of phytonutrients and vitamins. Antioxidant and antimicrobial properties help protect immune system and major organs from cellular damage. Increases blood circulation, metabolism and detoxification of blood stream.

VITAMIN & MINERAL

Vitamins – A, B1 (Thiamin), B2 (Riboflavin), B3 (Niacin), B6 (Pyridoxine), B9 (Folate), B12 (Cobalamin), C and E

Minerals – Iron, Copper, Manganese, Calcium, Chromium, Potassium and Magnesium

DISEASE PREVENTION

Excellent for skin conditions like eczema or psoriasis. May help prevent colon and colorectal cancer, indigestion, irritable bowel syndrome, ulcers and constipation. Juice may help reduce symptoms of joint disorders like rheumatoid and osteoarthritis. Alkaline nature soothes acid indigestion.

HOW TO GROW

Popular succulent is great to have during hot, sunny weather. Prefers warm climates and full sun. Choose plant with erect, healthy leaves. In mild climate, plant in a pot and bring inside to the warmest sunny spot indoors or in greenhouse. In warm, sunny weather put outside to help dry up excess moisture. Outdoors, it prefers great drainage and full sun. Amend planting soil with pebbles, compost/planting mix and sand. If soil naturally lacks good drainage, put in a raised bed. In a pot, must have 18 inches minimum depth. Water plants weekly, depending on soil moisture. Water less in humid or moist weather, more in warm, dry spells. Native to warm, dry areas. Tolerates dry weather well. Never over water, which causes root rot. Let soil dry out to 3-4 inches deep where soil begins to pull away from the sides before watering. Remove weeds to maintain proper pH and nutrient availability. Plant is good at foliar feeding. Apply foliar spray several times during growing season to maintain rigidity and spur healthy growth. When harvesting leaf for medicinal use, trim mature exterior leaves at the base. Leaves will not grow back following harvest. After some growth, plant produces baby plants around base. Pluck these out to replant or share with friends.

INSECT CONTROL

Extremely hardy. No known pests pose serious threat.

TIPS ✓ Avoid letting suckers (new shoots around the base) establish. They suck the life from the mother plant. Cut them at 3-4 inches in height, repot and water well to spur root growth. Makes a nice gift.

Apples

HEALTH POWER + Many effective antioxidants help decrease oxidative cell damage by free radicals. Contain dietary fiber and helpful phytonutrients called flavonoids, which have many different functions. Some act as antioxidants; some help maintain blood consistency without excess clotting; others help regulate blood pressure and reduce inflammation. Fiber stimulates healthy digestion and helps moderate the bad form of cholesterol (LDL), contributing to heart health.

VITAMIN & MINERAL ⬆ Vitamins – C
Minerals – traces

DISEASE PREVENTION 🚫 Phytonutrients help reduce risk of heart disease, asthma and female lung cancer. Early studies (lab and animal) suggest apples may reduce risk of colon, lung and breast cancer.

HOW TO GROW 🌱 One of the most popular, widespread and easily grown fruit trees in the world. Many different cultivars. Ask local nursery which cultivars best suited for your climate. Apples are self-sterile and need another variety to cross-pollinate to bear fruit. Growers often graft two varieties of a species onto one rootstock to produce fruit from only one tree. Many flavors to choose among. Different varieties best for cooking, eating fresh and making cider. Many patterns to train trees: fans, bush trees, dwarf pyramids, espaliers, cordons, stepovers, festooned trees or standard trees. Plant in spring or late fall. Trees prefer sunny, sheltered site with soil pH just above 6. Add lime to raise pH, if needed. Prepare soil by digging hole large enough to accept tree without altering root structure. Amend removed soil and around hole with organic matter and nutrients like aged compost or planting mix. Plant tree in style recommended for particular cultivar. Usually plants are bare-rooted or container grown. Some cultivars need ground stake for support. Water during dry weather and when apples begin to swell. Stop watering when apples begin to ripen. Apples are ripe and ready when a soft lift and twist removes them easily. Avoid bruising apples during harvest if you want them to store well. Discard any with signs of rot or disease. Store healthy apples, one variety to a bag with holes for airflow, in a cool place that will not freeze. During growth season, remove any apples that appear infected or dead. Thin out branches that block light from reaching interior of tree. Enjoy.

INSECT CONTROL ✕ Apple pests are aphids, wooly aphids, winter moths, coddling moth, apple sawfly and wasps. If pests threaten integrity of entire harvest, effective treatments are same as for aphids and sawflies on apricots. See Plums for dealing with wasps. Female winter moths have no wings and must crawl up tree to lay eggs between autumn and spring. Tie a sticky band around bottom of tree trunk during egg laying period. Wooly aphids cover themselves with wax-like lining, making them hard to remove with sprays. For large quantities building up, cut them out. Maggots inside apples probably come from coddling moths. Hang pheromone traps, which confuse males and keep them from finding females to fertilize eggs.

TIPS ✓ Apples harvest at two times. Early in summer just before they ripen. Left on tree they get soft and mushy. Harvest later varieties in fall or early winter. Apple trees take about two years to bear fruit. Reapply fertilizer over the roots each spring to stimulate nutritious development. Each winter, pick up fallen leaves to prevent fungus or disease from over wintering next to tree. Note: Eat the skin, which holds the beneficial nutrients. Another reason to grow organic apples with natural, uncontaminated skin.

Apricots

HEALTH POWER ➕ Good source of Vitamin A and beta-carotene. Antioxidant properties prevent free radicals from oxidizing the bad form of cholesterol (LDL), a first step in forming plaque in blood vessels. One form of Vitamin A, retinol, essential to light sensitivity. Impaired night vision early sign of deficiency. Good source of dietary fiber to support digestion, elimination and regulation of blood sugar.

VITAMIN & MINERAL

Vitamins – A and C
Minerals – Potassium, others in trace amounts

DISEASE PREVENTION

Reduces risk of macular degeneration, cataracts, heart disease, lung cancer, perhaps colon cancer. Vitamin A associated with reduced risk of cancer in organs lined with epithelial tissue.

HOW TO GROW

Many types of apricot cultivars; dwarfs and standard. Best depends on climate and space available. Dwarfs grow near 6 feet tall. If fan trained, grow to 15 feet. With minimal pruning, standard cultivars can reach 30 feet. If planting only one tree, use self-fruiting cultivar. Need sunny spot sheltered from wind. Soil should be well drained and fertile, with pH near 6. Prepare soil by working in plenty of organic matter and some plant mix two spades deep in radius as far as you think roots will spread. Be careful not to over fertilize with nutrients, which causes rapid growth and makes tree more susceptible to pests and disease. During growth, thin out branches that crowd the tree. Thinning heavily grouped fruits on a branch increases size of remaining fruits and prevents excess weight on branches. Produces fruit 2-3 years after sprouting. Ready to pick when soft. For dried apricots, pick while firm and split them.

INSECT CONTROL

Apricot pests include red spider mite, aphids, birds, sawfly, green fruit worm and peach tree borers. Tiny red spider mites problematic in dry weather, causing yellow spots on leaves and visible webs. Spray leaves regularly with insecticidal soap. Control aphids by planting French marigolds to attract predator ladybugs and hover flies. Also spray off with strong water stream. Repel birds by surrounding trees with netting. Distract birds by planting more appealing mulberry trees. Caterpillar stage of sawfly makes fruit inedible by boring holes. Control sawfly pupae by hoeing around bottom of tree to expose them for birds to eat. If large infestation, spray insecticide like Bt (Bacillus thuringiensis) or pyrethrum. Bt also controls green fruit worms. Look for small sawdust-like buildups next to holes. Probe into holes to kill borers.

TIPS

When selecting trees, choose one grafted to a seedling apricot rootstock. Generally grows better than ones grafted with other rootstocks. When thinning fruits, pick out central fruit first, as they tend to be odd shaped.

Arugula (Rugula, Rocket or Roquette)

HEALTH POWER +

Tasty leaves (nutty and/or peppery flavor) contain small quantities of many phytonutrients and vitamins. 4-5 cups give moderate to large dose. Cruciferous vegetable (similar to broccoli, Brussels sprouts, bok choy) helps prevent many cancers. Most benefit comes from phytonutrients. Glucosinolates and sulforaphanes help stimulate enzymes for detoxifying and removing cell-damaging (possibly carcinogenic) chemicals. Carotenes act as antioxidants to protect skin cells, blood vessel cells and others from sun and free-radical damage. Help ward off cancer and cardiovascular problems. Source of chlorophyll, present in all plants. Limited research on this phytonutrient. Some basic studies suggest chlorophyll may protect from carcinogenic chemicals eaten or created during metabolism. More carefully controlled research is needed to confirm link between chlorophyll and reduced cancer risk. Health benefits come from synergy of all or many nutrients with regular consumption.

VITAMIN & MINERAL ↑

Vitamins – K, A, C and B9 (Folate)
Minerals – Calcium, Manganese, Magnesium and Potassium

DISEASE PREVENTION ⊘

Regular eating linked with reduced risk of cardiovascular disease, cataracts, macular degeneration, many cancers (lung, colorectal, skin, perhaps others).

HOW TO GROW ✽

An easy-to-grow annual. Matures quickly (6-8 weeks). Likes cool weather and plenty of water. Sow seeds early spring and fall. Successive plantings OK through summer in cooler areas; through fall in warmer areas. Choose site with much sun. Soil wants good drainage. Enrich with much compost, manure or planting mix. Sow seeds thinly (1-2 inches apart) in rows spaced roughly 10 inches apart. Water regularly to keep soil moist. Take care not to over water. Ready to harvest when leaves are young and tender. Cut them and encourage plant to grow again. Make successive sowings every 2-3 weeks after first sowing. Watch out for sensitivity to hot weather; makes plant go to seed. Avoid growing during heat waves or plant in partial shade.

INSECT CONTROL ✕ Resistant to common insect pests and diseases. Susceptible to slugs or snails. Early morning or evening, remove by hand. Or embed cup of beer in soil; lures them to crawl in and drown.

TIPS ✓ Harvest leaves while young. Older, larger leaves tough and bitter. Works well added to soups and salads or as garnish.

Asparagus

HEALTH POWER + Improves digestion by increasing number and health of good bacteria in large intestine that suppress harmful bacteria. Promotes overall health with wide range of nutrients. Amino acid asparagine is a natural diuretic. Used to reduce swelling; may help diminish premenstrual water retention. Contains B vitamin folate (more than 50 percent RDA), a crucial nutrient for normal fetal development during pregnancy. Helps avoid birth defects by helping DNA synthesize and replicate properly. Pyridoxine promotes heart health by lowering homocysteine levels in the blood stream.

VITAMIN & MINERAL ↑ Vitamins – K, B9 (Folate), C, A, B1 (Thiamin), B2 (Riboflavin), B6 (Pyridoxine) and B3 (Niacin)
Minerals – Manganese, Copper, Phosphorus, Potassium, Iron, Zinc, Magnesium, Selenium and Calcium

DISEASE PREVENTION ⊘ High Vitamin B9 (folate) concentration helps reduce risk of heart disease by lowering high levels of homocysteine in the blood; converts homocysteine to cysteine. Asparagus also has phytonutrients that may prevent growth of many cancer cell lines (notably colon cancer).

HOW TO GROW  A perennial plant needing initial investment but offering valuable returns. Choose plot with plenty of sunshine and exceptional drainage. Amend soil with compost or quality planting mix for loam with good air space, drainage and nutrient availability. In heavy soil, work in more compost or planting mix to raise bed slightly. Soil pH should be above 6; add lime as needed. Start from seed or buy plants with one-year-old root crowns from a reliable nursery, saving the first year of effort. Dig a trench 6 inches deep and 1 foot wide, with center raised a little. Soak root crowns in water for 1 hour. Plant one foot apart, making sure to spread roots around the slightly raised center of trench. First year, water well, never depriving plants of water. Each spring, apply more mix rich in organic matter and micronutrients. In fall, mulch around plant with compost or balanced planting mix. Full harvest comes two years from crown stage or three years from seed. Begin harvest in second year (after planting crowns) when shoots grow more than 5 inches. Harvest all but a few shoots by cutting or snapping them just below ground shortly before tip opens. Be careful not to hurt crowns when you cut.

INSECT CONTROL ✕ Asparagus rust, slugs and asparagus beetles are most common pests. Beetles controlled by hand removing. If seriously infested, spray or dust with rotenone. Avoid asparagus rust (rust-colored spots on leaves and stems) by buying resistant strains from trusted nursery. Slugs controlled several ways. Physically remove and dispose each morning or night. Sink saucers of beer into soil to attract and drown. When plants are still small, cut off plastic bottles and secure over plants. Spread a thin layer of lime or soot around plant to repel slugs.

TIPS ✓ To preserve soil balance, start new bed every 10 years. (Three years before discontinuing old one to avoid missing a season of tasty, fresh, home-grown asparagus.) To avoid crown rot, do not let crowns lie in bed of water. Slightly raised beds help prevent this.

Avocados

HEALTH POWER ✚ Delectable fruit high in monounsaturated fats (the good ones). These lipids help reduce LDLs and raise HDLs. Also rich in beta-Sitosterol, a natural substance that lowers blood cholesterol level. High levels of potassium in avocados also can help reduce elevated blood pressure. Folate is great for circulatory health and normal neural development in fetuses. Avocados also contain the fat soluble phytonutrients carotenoids and tocopherols, potent antioxidants and anti-carcinogens.

VITAMIN & MINERAL ↑ Vitamins – K, B9 (Folate), B6 (Pyridoxine), C and E (Tocopherols)
Minerals – Potassium and Copper

Bad cholesterol and triglyceride lowering effects help prevent heart disease. Folate helps prevent atherosclerosis. Avocados linked to preventing oral and prostate cancers. Carotenoids and tocopherols are fat-soluble and synergistically inhibit growth of these cancer cells. Source of good fats in avocado also provides medium for absorption of these phytonutrients in the intestine, rendering avocado an all-around health promoter.

DISEASE PREVENTION

Grow on trees of various cultivars (same plant with slightly different characteristics). Origin is tropical; flourish in warmer climates. Varieties have slightly different tolerances and ripen at different times. Ask local nursery which work best in your climate. Choose several different kinds for maximum production. Plant in spacious location with full day's sun to grow up to 40 feet high. If winter freezes over, plant tree in pot at least 2 feet in diameter and bring into garage during cold months. In milder climates, dig a hole 3 feet wide by 3 feet deep. Tree needs regular deep watering with superb drainage to prevent root rot. If soil is heavy and dense, amend with coarse organic materials to get thorough draining. Sprinkle a few handfuls of plant mix in and plant in the hole. Do not plant too deeply; avocados have shallow root networks. Mulch area generously to extend interval between waterings. Keep soil moist but not wet.

HOW TO GROW

Pests rarely hamper fruit production on fully developed trees. Young trees need protection from large infestation. Most common insects: avocado loopers, pyriform scale, dictyospermum scale, avocado red mites, borers and lace bugs. As a last resort only, spray low-toxic, organic pesticides-fungicides: soaps, oils or Bt.

INSECT CONTROL

Avocados prone to scab disease. Have nursery staff help choose resistant strain. Pinch terminal roots to keep tree in check. Fast growing; need aggressive trimming to keep nice shape.

TIPS

Bananas

HEALTH POWER

Excellent source and high doses of potassium, vitamin C and fiber at low cost with low sodium, fat and cholesterol. Potassium essential for nerve and muscle functions and to control blood pressure. High fiber promotes healthy heart, lowers total cholesterol, adds bulk to stool and speeds up digestive process. Fiber also helps regulate blood sugars by holding onto carbohydrates in intestine and slowing down absorption of sugar into blood system, which lowers stress on insulin-producing pancreatic cells. Special banana fiber, pectin, promotes normal digestion and nutrient absorption. Promotes stomach health by building strong inner lining and eliminating ulcer-causing bacteria. Bananas have compounds (fructooligosaccharides and short-chain fatty acids) that feed helpful intestinal bacteria.

VITAMIN & MINERAL

Vitamins – B6 (Pyridoxine) and C
Minerals – Potassium and Manganese

DISEASE PREVENTION

May help reduce symptoms or onset of atherosclerosis, heart disease, stroke, diabetes, ulcers, breast cancer, and colon cancer. Bananas, like cabbage and other root vegetables, have high concentrations of phenolic compounds that help reduce cancer in animals, possibly in humans.

HOW TO GROW

Many varieties. (If above zone 10, choose cultivar that tolerates cooler temp.) Fruit develops best with long, humid, warm growing season. Misting leaves morning and evening helps nurture. Choose warm site with dark, highly fertile, well-drained soil and full day's sun. Needs shelter from wind. Plant is self-fertile; only one plant needed to bear fruit. Local nursery usually has banana suckers or baby trees in containers. Plant trees in well-amended soil 10 feet apart (or more depending on how large cultivar grows). Keep soil moist throughout growth, but avoid standing water. Adding fertilizer (compost tea, manure tea or other) helps meet high demand for nutrients. Many suckers sprout from base to create more plants. Prune off all but one or two to concentrate energy for fruiting. Control weeds by hand pulling and laying down compost mulch or other material to retain moisture and deter weeds. Takes 9 months to fully plump up and ready for harvest. Although green, will ripen to yellow. Need little pruning to remove dead plant matter. After harvesting, cut down banana tree, leaving sucker that produced bananas. It develops into new tree to renew growing process.

INSECT CONTROL

Pests will differ depending on the area where you grow. Banana aphids, spider mites, weevils, rose beetles, flower and red rust thrips, whitefly and mealy bugs. Talk with nursery to see what may cause local problems and how to treat.

TIPS	✓	After 6 months, when flower opens and male fingers fall to the ground, remove purple flowers and stem about 6-8 inches below last female fingers. (Fingers become bananas.) Growing bananas in cooler climates may be risky, as frost kills growth above ground. To protect from freezing, cut down plant and cover with mulch and sheet of black polypropylene.

Basil

HEALTH POWER	+	Basil known for flavonoids (protect DNA, which creates and regulates cells) and volatile oils (antibacterial action). Some oils even halt growth of drug-resistant bacteria. Volatile oil eugenol may reduce inflammation and pain, such as in arthritis.
VITAMIN & MINERAL	↑	Vitamins – K, A and C Minerals – Iron, Calcium, Manganese, Magnesium and Potassium
DISEASE PREVENTION	⃠	Basil contains strong antioxidant beta-carotene. Prevents unstable molecules (free radicals) from damaging epithelial cells including blood vessel walls. Beta-carotene helps prevent plaque build up (atherosclerosis) in arterial walls by blocking oxidation of LDL cholesterol. Lowers risk of heart attack and stroke. Contributes to the prevention of asthma, rheumatoid and osteoarthritis.
HOW TO GROW	☙	Grow as an annual where winter snow or frost are common; a perennial in warm, Southern regions. Two types: sweet and bush. Sweet is taller (1.5-2 feet high, more productive, better flavor). Sweet basil grows best in sunny, protected area with healthy soil. Sow seeds in early spring in smaller containers indoors. Prepare soil by working in aged compost, manure or planting mix with plenty of organic matter. Transplant outdoors about one foot apart after last frost. Keep soil moist; water thoroughly during hot, dry weather. Remove flower buds when they appear to stimulate more

growth. Harvest younger leaves through summer in quantities needed for cooking. Also dry and put in airtight containers or freeze for later use.

INSECT CONTROL ✗ Minor pest problems. Prevent Japanese beetles from eating foliage by hand picking.

TIPS ✓ Save seeds for next year by harvesting stems after seeds ripen. Hang upside down in a closed area. Set cloth underneath to catch seeds as plant dries up and releases them

Beans

HEALTH POWER ✚ Among many varieties, pinto beans are surprisingly nutritious. More fiber than most foods. Excellent at lowering cholesterol, regulating blood sugar (especially for those with insulin resistance) and smoothing out digestion. Crucial contribution to heart health. High content of folate, potassium and magnesium. Folate lowers concentration of amino acid homocysteine. (When elevated in the blood, can seriously damage blood vessels.) Potassium an essential component of nerve cell communication, muscle contraction (especially heart) and blood pressure regulation. Magnesium helps maintain blood flow through vessels by blocking calcium channels. Iron optimizes oxygen attachment to hemoglobin molecules, which transport oxygen in blood. Copper and manganese help protect energy-producing cell bodies (mitochondria) by activating superoxide dismutase, which knocks out free radicals. Copper also needed to form hemoglobin. Vitamin B1 (thiamin) contributes to energy production and healthy brain function by helping produce neurotransmitter acetylcholine. Excellent source of protein at low calorie cost.

VITAMIN & MINERAL ⬆ Vitamins – B9 (Folate) and B1 (Thiamin)
Minerals – Molybdenum, Manganese, Phosphorus, Iron, Magnesium, Potassium and Copper

DISEASE PREVENTION ⊘ Reduces risk of heart attack, stroke, cardiovascular disease, irritable bowel syndrome, diabetes, colon cancer and Alzheimer's disease.

🐚 Part of the Leguminosae family. Hundreds of different cultivars. You can find a variety that will grow in your location. Two main types: shell beans used for seeds and snap/bush beans grown for their pods. Two types of growth patterns: self-supporting and others (pole and runner beans) that grow on stakes or suspended strings. Most beans grow best in warmer temperatures (about 75°F) and are very sensitive to cooler temperatures. Prefer sheltered sunny site with well-drained soil and lots of organic matter. Prepare rows by amending soil with aged compost or planting mix rich in organic matter. If soil is heavy, use more compost to loosen. For seeds to sow properly, soil should be above 60°F and near pH 6.5. Beans do not easily transplant, but if warm season is short, you may have no choice. Start beans indoors in pots about a month before frost. Sow seeds outdoors about two weeks after the last frost. Place them about 1 inch under the soil and pat the soil down over top. Place bush beans 4-6 inches apart in rows and space rows about 2.5 feet apart. Pole beans are more sensitive to cold. Plan on planting a week or two later and harvesting a week or two earlier. Yield about three times as many beans per area as bush types. Sow seeds 2 inches deep and 10-12 inches apart in single rows spaced about 3.5 feet apart or double rows spaced 1 foot apart. A bean tee-pee makes nice addition to garden. Water beds evenly and keep soil moist. Letting soil dry out may hurt yields. Bush types germinate in 1 week; pole types in 2 weeks. After seedlings are a few inches tall, apply a thick layer of mulch to retain moisture, deter weeds and buffer the soil against temperature fluctuations. Light application of fertilizer containing micronutrients mid-season produces high yields. Snap beans and shell beans ready for harvest when soft and a little longer than index finger. Harvest all as soon as they are ready to stimulate re-growth. If you see outlines of seeds on pod, you have waited too long. Eat or freeze them immediately to preserve the fresh flavor. Both unshelled beans and those in pods preserve for about a week in refrigerator. To dry shell types, let them sit in pods on plants until pods turn brown and dry out. If weather is wet, cut plant and hang upside down in dry area. Dried beans last about one year.

✕ Common pests are aphids, corn earworms, cabbage loopers, corn borers, Mexican beetles and Japanese beetles. Aphids can be handled by inter-planting French Marigolds, which attract their predators. Hoverflies and ladybugs eat tons of aphids. Corn earworms grow roughly 2 feet long and grub on bean plants. Not a large threat, but if you get a manually uncontrollable infestation, apply the insecticide Bacillus thuringiensis (Bt).

Cabbage loopers feed on leaves and eat twice their body weight a day. If they are uncontrollable by manually picking, use an insecticide like Bt. Mexican beetles will ravage the bean plants if they infest in numbers. The first sign is small yellow groups of eggs, which hatch into larvae that look like small yellow caterpillars. Adults look like larger, darker ladybugs. Remove eggs and larvae and smash adults when you see them.

TIPS ✓ In order to get continuous harvest, successively sow every two weeks until 2 months before first frost. Be careful not to knock off blossoms when watering.

Beets

HEALTH POWER + A great vegetable for defending against cell damage in digestive tract. Color comes from betacyanin, which prevents pre-cancerous cell damage. Fiber induces liver production of antioxidants (glutathione peroxidase and glutathione S-transferase) for detoxifying body from damaging, potentially carcinogenic chemicals. Stimulate production of immune cells in animal colon and protect from damage by nitrosamines (created from nitrates) in stomach. Phytonutrients choline and its metabolite betaine correlate with lower levels of C-reactive protein, tumor necrosis factor alpha and homocysteine. All help reduce inflammation and blood vessel damage, loss of cognitive function and insulin resistance. Folate deters blood vessel damage by lowering concentrations of homocysteine and prevents neural tube defects in fetus. Lowers total cholesterol and triglyceride levels, which is great for the cardiovascular system. Magnesium assures calcium absorption in gastrointestinal tract. Calcium helps make healthy bones. Iron essential for hemoglobin to deliver oxygen to all body tissues.

VITAMIN & MINERAL ↑ Vitamins – B9 (Folate) and C
Minerals – Manganese, Potassium, Magnesium, Iron, Copper and Phosphorus

DISEASE PREVENTION ⊘ Beets lower risk of heart disease, colon cancer, stomach cancer, birth defects, type II diabetes, osteoporosis and anemia.

HOW TO GROW

Beets prefer a deep soil rich in organic matter, microbes and nutrients. Work in some aged compost or planting mix to both fertilize and improve drainage. Like other root vegetables, they benefit from raised beds but not needed if soil is naturally deep and worked well. Grow best at 60-65°F. If summer is scorching, grow beets in winter/early spring and fall. Prefer full sun, but in hotter areas, part shade prevents scorching. Seeds come in groupings; one "seed" is a group of 7-8 seeds. When soil is workable, create shallow drills at 1 foot apart or more. Rinse seeds vigorously in a filter or soak overnight to promote germination. One month before the last frost, sow each cluster of seeds 1 inch deep and 2.5 inches apart within the drills. Since each seed is a cluster, thin out seedlings by pulling up roots. Once seedlings reach a few inches tall, thin out to about 6 inches between plants. For continual harvest, sow the seeds successively every couple weeks until weather heats up (midsummer). Keep beds weed free, but be careful not to damage roots. Mulch between plants with compost or other organic matter. Last sowings will be the main crop. Keep soil moist by watering roughly one inch a week or more during hot stretches. Harvest early ones when they are smaller (ping pong ball size) and later ones when they reach baseball size. When separating leaves from beet, make sure not to damage skin. Leave about an inch of the stems on so they don't bleed. Store some undamaged ones for winter in a container surrounded by peat, sand, vermiculite or sawdust.

INSECT CONTROL

Grown in healthy conditions, usually develop pest free. You may see flea beetles (small, dark creatures that jump up when approached) and leaf miners (tiny black insects that burrow into the leaf leaving yellow tunnels). To rid crop of flea beetles, cut out a rectangular card (plastic or cardboard) and cover one side with sticky material (thick grease works). Slowly run the sticky side of card about an inch above plants and watch flea beetles jump up and get stuck to the card. Leaf miners are tiny black insects that burrow into the leaf, leaving yellow tunnels. Remove the leaves and destroy them as soon as you notice them.

TIPS

Key to tender beets is to grow quickly and harvest when they reach full size. To encourage growth, fertilize every few weeks with compost tea or liquid seaweed extract.

Blackberries

HEALTH POWER +

Blackberries are a great source of antioxidants. Some fall in the groups of polyphenols and anthocyanins, both known to help fight against free radicals that cause damage to blood vessels, heart disease and many types of cancer. Anthocyanins give the deep color. Blackberries are also solid sources of vitamin C and magnesium. Vitamin C, an antioxidant, helps maintain healthy immune system by protecting cells from oxidative damage. C helps reactivate vitamin E, a fat-soluble antioxidant in fatty tissue/liquids. Trace mineral magnesium promotes bone health by increasing the absorption of calcium and the proper functioning of all cells. Great source of fiber, promoting smooth, healthy digestion, regulating blood sugar and lowering cholesterol. Vitamin A protects eyesight, boosts immune system and maintains elasticity in epithelial cells inside internal organs, especially blood vessels.

VITAMIN & MINERAL ↑

Vitamins – C, K, E, B9 (Folate), A and B3 (Niacin)
Minerals – Manganese, Copper, Potassium and Magnesium

DISEASE PREVENTION ⊘

Medical research (but not clinical studies) suggests blackberries in the diet may help prevent cardiovascular disease, lung inflammation, clotting deficiency, diabetes and many types of cancer especially colon, breast and cervical.

HOW TO GROW

Blackberries have extensive growth range. Varieties grow in the Deep South, while others endure harsh northern winters. Self-fertile, so only one variety needed for fruit. Plant in early spring or early fall. Choose a soil site with plenty of sun. Blackberries prefer deep rich soil that holds lots of moisture yet drains well. Needs pH 6 or just below. Work in plenty of well-aged compost and/or planting mix rich in organic matter, especially if soil is sandier loam. Dig a hole about 1.5 feet deep and 2 feet wide. Place compost or planting mix in the bottom, followed by the blackberry plant. Refill the hole with amended soil and top off with a couple handfuls of nutrient-dense fertilizer like seaweed extract or bone meal. If planting more than one, separate trenches by about 10 feet. Trim plant down to about 6 inches tall after planting. To train, use wire and two 6-foot posts per row. Place the posts roughly 5 feet outside the last plant in each row.

Connect the two posts with the first wire about 3 feet up the posts. Successively place more wires to the top of the posts at 12-18 inch intervals. During first year, regularly train shoots to one side of the post. The following year, train new growing shoots to the other side. This keeps new growth away from the fruiting wood. In late winter, place a mulch layer of compost, manure or other all-encompassing source of nutrients around the bushes. After harvesting fruit, cut the fruit bearing shoots down to the ground.

INSECT CONTROL ✕ Blackberry pests are aphids, raspberry beetles, Japanese beetles and birds. See Strawberries for aphid control. Raspberry beetle larvae feed on fruit as it ripens. They are seen when fruit appears damaged. The only way to treat is to spray an insecticide like pyrethrum when the flowers open. Be careful not to use an insecticide that kills bees, which pollinate the flowers. Japanese beetles are a shiny blue-green color about one-half inch in size. Shake them off the plant early in the morning, set out baited traps, and/or apply floating row covers. Floating row covers also stop birds, which can eat a lot of berries in one session.

TIPS ✓ Make blackberries a part of your fruit intake.

Blueberries

HEALTH POWER ✚ Blueberries top the antioxidant list of major fruits and vegetables. They have more highly effective antioxidants than a glass of red wine. Multiple different vitamins, minerals and nutrients work together to give this fruit many potential health benefits with few calories. Antioxidants (the anthocyanidins) disarm free radicals and prevent damage to the collagen network (the backbone of cells keeping them stable and durable for proper functioning). Also help prevent heart problems, ulcers and vision loss. Protect and maintain proper cell structure in blood vessels. Contain both soluble and insoluble fibers to help control blood sugar spikes, lower cholesterol and support digestion. May increase brain function to improve learning ability and muscle coordination. Adding blueberries to your diet does wonders for your overall health.

| VITAMIN & MINERAL | ⬆ | Vitamins – Vitamin C, K, E and others in small quantities
Minerals – Manganese, Iron, Calcium and others in small quantities |

| DISEASE PREVENTION | ⊘ | Preventing free radical damage may help the brain avoid conditions associated with aging, like Alzheimer's, dementia and osteoporosis. Many studies suggest blueberries help deter heart disease, macular degeneration, peptic ulcers, varicose veins and many types of cancer (especially colon and ovarian). Also contain many phytonutrients which help prevent urinary tract infections and digestive system inflammation. |

| HOW TO GROW | ☙ | Native to North America, aesthetically pleasing and naturally pest tolerant, these nutrient-rich, delicious little nibbles are popular among home gardeners. Aside from preference in taste or texture, soil requirements keep gardeners from growing this super food everywhere. Bushes come in forms that grow short with smaller berries and a tall, higher yielding type with larger berries. Crosses have height and berry size falling between. In warmer climates, rabbit eye blueberries are popular. These grow more than 10 feet tall, sometimes higher than 20 feet, and can yield up to 20 pounds of fruit each. Tall bush berries are most popular in home growing. Blueberries are particular about growing conditions, so initial testing may be needed to find suitable spot. Grow best in well-drained soils with loose loam or sandier base. Prefer slightly acidic soil pH around 4.5-5.5. If soil is basic, lower it by mixing in sphagnum, peat moss or compost made from oak, hemlock bark or pine. Avoid aluminum sulfate, which kills certain soil creatures and changes the taste of fruit. Another soil fix: Grow in raised beds, which are fine for blueberry's shallow root system. Prefer a sunny spot. Since they cannot self fertilize, plant at least two cultivars to yield fruit. Mix in a handful of planting mix suitable for maintaining soil pH per square yard before planting. Plant tall bushes and rabbit eyes 5 feet apart in rows spaced roughly 8 feet apart. Low bush plants should be placed 1 foot apart in rows 3 feet or more apart. Apply a thick layer of mulch around the plants every year. Mulch derived from oak, pine, woodchips or hemlock will help support soil pH. Near the end of winter, add a second application of organic fertilizer (well-aged manure or compost) rich in nitrogen that also supports the acidic pH. Fertilizers with fish bone, seaweed, or cottonseed meal are excellent sources of micronutrients as well as phosphorus and nitrogen. Water regularly to keep the soil moist especially during drought periods, as blueberries dry out quickly. During growth, remove any weak branches or damaged growth |

to conserve energy and prevent infestations. Keep the bush from growing too thick by removing branches to leave at least a few inches for light and air to get in. Berries are generally ripe and ready for harvest about a week after they turn blue. Tasting is the best way to tell. Leftovers can be frozen for later use. In fall each year, trim the tips of all branches.

INSECT CONTROL ✕ Home growers have few problems with pests. Cherry fruit worm or blueberry maggot may cause problems by burrowing inside berries to make them inedible. Remove any berries showing signs of infestation or damage. Clear your plot of any rotting fruit before winter. If insects become a serious problem, dust with an organically approved Bt or rotenone. Birds are the largest worry with ripening fruits. Hold them out by constructing a shelter of strong netting with small perforations around the bushes, which keep birds from entering.

TIPS ✓ Blueberries take 5-7 years to reach full yields, but you can get a head start by purchasing 2-3-year-old plants. Inter-planting blueberries with other species of flowers that attract pollinating insects helps increase chances for pollination. Test to see if ripe (berries come off easily with a slight twist). Easy to grow, but treated as a luxury item in stores because they are hard to keep perfect when shipped.

Bok Choy

HEALTH POWER ✚ Bok choy is another crucifer (like broccoli, cauliflower and cabbage) with many beneficial phytonutrients. Also zero fats and low carbohydrate count. Most researched are the glucosinolates and carotenoids. Glucosinolates are a mixed blessing from plants. In high doses, they can inhibit thyroid hormone, which is needed for proper cell metabolism. In moderate amounts, they block cancer cells by directly affecting the cell cycle and protecting against harmful free radicals. Isothiocyanates, some derived from glucosinolates, are other powerful agents preventing cancer cells from forming and proliferating. Bok choy is an excellent source of many carotenoids, especially beta-carotene, an antioxidant throughout the body. Studies suggest beta-carotene lowers cancer risk and is great for the eyes. (More research needed to prove these claims.) Bok choy is especially high in vitamins A, C and K, with some folate and vitamin B6. A and

C are antioxidants that protect immune cells, prevent plaque build up in arteries and help preserve elasticity of epithelial tissue (especially blood vessel walls). Folate and vitamin B6 lower blood plasma homocysteine, linked with vessel damage at high concentration.

VITAMIN & MINERAL

Vitamins – A, C, K, B9 (Folate), and B6 (Pyridoxine)
Minerals – Calcium, Potassium and Manganese

DISEASE PREVENTION

Bok choy may help prevent heart disease, macular degeneration, cancers of colon, prostate, endometrial lining, lung and pancreas. Potentially reduces risk of many other cancers.

HOW TO GROW

Known as Chinese cabbage, requires same soil preparation as other Brassicas (members of the mustard family; broccoli, cabbage, cauliflower) but are more demanding than other cabbages. See one of these entries for soil prep. Choose a site with full sun. Plan to grow them next to other Brassicas in their own bed with extra compost, manure or planting mix worked in. Sow seeds beginning late spring or about three months before the first intense frost. Place seeds two every 8-10 inches in shallow drills spaced 1 foot apart. Later, thin out to leave most prominent seedling every 8-10 inches. Does not store long. For continuous harvest, sow seeds every two weeks. Keep soil moist and weed free. Hoe and water regularly. Crops are ready to harvest 2-3 months after sowing.

INSECT CONTROL

Slugs, earwigs and flea beetles are common pests. Try to remove and destroy pests by hand. Slugs feed in twilight, morning and evening. If infestation seems severe, try another method. For snails and slugs, embed a cup of beer in the soil. Both will be attracted, slither their way in, get stuck and drown. Earwigs attack by nipping at buds and leaves of plants. Generally, not a problem, but if needed, you can easily set a trap. They don't like daylight. Create a dark environment by filling a pot with dry grass, leaves or plant material and perching it upside down on a skinny post above the affected plants. Earwigs will crawl in during the day. Destroy the plant matter inside the pot every week or so. Control tiny flea beetles by using their instinctive responses against them. Like fleas, they spring up in the air when approached. Create a sticky piece of wood or cardboard by applying grease or other adhesive that will remain sticky. Walk along the plants with the sticky side a couple inches above the foliage. Watch them jump and get stuck.

To get the most nutritional benefit from bok choy, change how you prepare it. When left raw, the glucosinolates are more bio-available. When cooked lightly with a little oil, the carotenoids are more available for absorption. Golden Rule: diversify your diet. Get many different fruits, veggies and other sources of nutrition worked into the weekly menu.

Broccoli

HEALTH POWER +

Broccoli is a super food with many vitamins, minerals and phytonutrients that trigger a complex, intricate set of biochemical pathways supporting overall health. High fiber content lowers concentration of low-density lipoproteins (LDL) in the blood and elevated blood sugar, promoting cardiovascular health. Helps promote weight loss. A superior source of antioxidants. Folate helps protect the heart/circulatory system and promote healthy fetal development. Contains sulforaphane, which fights Helicobacter pylori bacteria that can cause stomach cancer. Along with isothiocyanate, it also boosts production of detoxification enzymes, which can help rid the body of potentially carcinogenic chemicals. Speeds up metabolism of estrogen, which may help suppress breast cancer. The phytonutrient indole-3-carbinol in broccoli reduces the metastasis of cancer cells and risk of breast cancer. Other beneficial phytonutrients include carotenoids, flavonoids and glucosinolates (which get converted to sulforaphane). Great source of calcium for bone building. Vitamin C, beta-carotene and the enzyme cofactors zinc and selenium help maintain strong immune system.

VITAMIN & MINERAL ⬆

Vitamins – C, K, A, B9 (Folate), B6 (Pyridoxine), B2 (Riboflavin), B5 (Pantothenic), B1 (Thiamin), B3 (Niacin) and E
Minerals – Manganese, Potassium, Phosphorus, Magnesium, Iron, Calcium & Zinc

DISEASE PREVENTION ⊘

Lowers risk of atherosclerosis, heart disease, stroke, anemia, osteoporosis, cataracts, lung cancer, stomach cancer, breast cancer, bladder cancer, ovarian cancer, colon cancer, colorectal cancer, prostate cancer and potentially many more.

HOW TO
GROW

In the Brassica family, broccoli is one of the most popular, easy-to-grow vegetables. Start from seed or find good local nursery to get disease-free transplant. Broccoli grows best in cool climates where daytime temperature remains below 70°F. Choose soil that has drainage, good aeration and plenty of sun. Place plant where it will not cast a shadow on another that needs the sun, as broccoli can grow up to 3 feet tall. A pH between 6.2 and 7 is good. If higher, lime the soil to reduce. Mix in well-aged compost or manure. Broccoli has high nutrient demand. Add a couple fistfuls of plant mix with alfalfa, fish bone, and feather meal per yard to ensure nourishment. If you start with seeds, sow them about a month and a half before planting outside. Plant seedlings or transplants 20-30 inches apart. Keep soil moist by watering regularly. (Avoid water logging.) Keep soil weed free by pulling, mulching with organic matter or putting down black plastic as last resort.

**INSECT
CONTROL**

Broccoli is affected by many common pests and diseases. Most significant is caterpillar stage of white cabbage butterfly, root maggots, flea beetles and aphids. A plastic row cover protects from the first three. Use an insecticidal soap or limonene spray to repel aphids. Remove pests when you see them. If physical removal doesn't work, organic pesticide is a must. If caterpillars are resilient, spray Bacillus thuringiensis (Bt), an organic agent that is safe for pets, humans and other garden plants.

TIPS

When harvesting, cut the central shoot first to promote outgrowth of side shoots. This maximizes production of the edible vegetable portion. When cooking, the crunchier the better. If you let cooked broccoli get soggy, most nutrients are lost. To prevent club root disease, never grow Brassicas in the same plot year after year.

Brussels Sprouts

**HEALTH
POWER**

Brussels sprouts contain phytonutrients that assist a range of functions. Contain sulfur compounds like sulforaphane, which triggers vital detoxification enzymes in the liver. Also an excellent source of vitamins C, A, folate, fiber and other phytonutrients, all promoting healthy skin, digestion, immune function, cardiovascular function, fetal development and overall health.

VITAMIN & MINERAL

Vitamins – K, C, B9 (Folate), A, B6 (Pyridoxine), B1 (Thiamin), B2 (Riboflavin) & E

Minerals – Manganese, Potassium, Iron, Phosphorus, Magnesium and Copper

DISEASE PREVENTION

By increasing detoxification and reducing DNA damage, crucifers like Brussels sprouts reduce the symptoms or onset of many cancers more effectively than any other fruit or vegetable. Cancer examples: prostate, colon, bladder, breast and lung. The sulfur-containing phytonutrients slow or stop cell division of cancer cells and programmed cell death.

HOW TO GROW

Brussels sprouts take up extra space, but you can get varieties that last through fall and others that last through winter for a prolonged harvest. Choose site with full sun and well-drained soil. Soil pH needs to be 6.5 to 7; add lime to raise, if needed. Amend soil with highly fertile planting mix. Sow seeds in shallow drills 6 inches apart three to four months before the first expected frost. When they reach a few inches tall, plant them out centered in spaces 2-3 feet square depending on how large you want sprouts to be. Compress the well you plant into. Water initially and wait 1-2 weeks before repeating. Cover spaces between plants with compost, mulch or plastic to reduce weeds and need for watering. Keep watered through summer. In fall, pick off yellow leaves to avoid spreading disease. Harvest Brussels sprouts from the bottom up starting in early fall once they have hardened.

INSECT CONTROL

Brussels sprouts are affected by a number of common garden pests, including cabbage butterflies, club, cabbage root maggot, cabbage moth, cabbage loopers and cabbage worms. Handpick and dispose of pests as they appear. Morning and evening are best times to remove. If infestation is uncontrollable manually, use insecticidal soap. Bt works in some instances. Sink shallow cups of beer in soil to induce slugs and snails to climb in and drown. Floating row covers protect against birds. If uncertain what to do, capture some pests and ask your local nursery for advice on best organic treatment.

TIPS ✓ Best use of space may be to interplant another crop in the spaces between Brussels sprout plants. If you do, use little fertilizer as flooding Brussels sprouts with fertilizer softens them. If site gets windy, staking may be necessary to prevent toppling. Frost is not a problem and can even enhance taste, but if not insulated by snow, even the toughest sprouts will suffer with a hard freeze. You may need a season of trial and error to find the best planting time to get the healthiest yielding plants. Cook by steaming lightly to retain nutrients.

Burdock

HEALTH POWER ➕ Burdock has been used for centuries as an alternative herbal medicine. Diuretic (urine producing) properties help "flush" the body as it removes excess water. Some cancer patients say it enhances quality of life. Found in popular cancer remedies like Essiac and Hoxsey formula. May lower blood glucose levels, which helps prevent and manage diabetes. Useful in treating skin conditions (wounds, eczema, acne and psoriasis) by mixing into a cream-like lotion and applying directly to clean skin. Reduces throat pain and is found in some cold medicines. Detoxifies liver, kidneys, gallbladder and lymph system. Fiber stimulates digestive tract, helping relieve constipation. Side effects include dry mouth, slowed absorption of nutrients like iron, laxative action and slower heart rate. Not recommended if you take prescription drugs or are pregnant. (Can stimulate uterus.)

VITAMIN & MINERAL ⬆ Vitamins – B6 (Pyridoxine), B9 (Folate) and C
Minerals – Manganese, Magnesium, Potassium, Calcium, Copper and Iron

DISEASE PREVENTION 🚫 May help reduce symptoms or onset of diabetes, gout, ulcers, rheumatoid and osteoarthritis, acne, psoriasis and potentially many cancers.

HOW TO GROW 🌱 A great leafy vegetable native to Europe and Asia. Very efficient because both roots and shoot are edible. Hardy and able to grow in variety of climates (warm and humid to cool and dry). In cold winters (down to 0°F), plant loses leaves but regenerates them in spring. Sub-zero may compromise roots. Prefers well-drained, deep soil with light, sandy loam for deep rooting. Choose site with full sun. Needs soil pH close to 7 for best nutrient uptake. When preparing soil, avoid working in compost or manure, which may cause roots to fork out. Phosphorus helps spur root growth. Plant in site composted for previous crop and work in some ground rock phosphate or fish bone meal. When soil warms up (usually in spring), soak seeds for a half day to prepare for germination. Plant out directly about ¾ inch deep. Space or thin plants to 10 inches apart in rows 10 inches apart. Water regularly at first to keep surface moist. Seedlings pop up in about 2 weeks. A week after that, change watering regime to one deep watering weekly to promote downward root growth. (Roots go as deep as 2-3 feet.) When seedlings grow more than a few inches, mulch around plants to retain moisture and deter weeds. Harvest during any part of development. Expect roots to mature near end of summer or early autumn. Loosen soil around roots without damaging. Carefully wiggle roots out by pulling on tops. Harvest when mature, or they get too woody to eat.

INSECT CONTROL ✕ Common pests are nematodes. To prevent, plant French marigolds (Tagetes patula) or Mexican marigolds (Tagetes minuta). Work them into soil and let rot before planting burdock.

TIPS ✓ Young roots are eaten raw similar to radish with a little salt. Older roots used more for cooking. Can be stir-fried, roasted, braised, pickled, added to soups, made into tea or used in a drink. Young leafy portions can be eaten as a green in salads and sandwiches.

Cabbage

HEALTH POWER ✚ Similar to Brussels sprouts, cruciferous vegetables like cabbage increase the production and action of enzymes that detoxify the body. Beyond antioxidant action that removes dangerous free radicals, crucifers make DNA produce more detoxification and anti-cancer enzymes. Enhance natural defenses by stimulating production of antioxidant compounds like glutathione. Supply sulfur compounds like sinigrin and sulforaphane that catalyze production of anti-carcinogens. Also affect the expression of cancer-related genes. Amino acid glutamine helps restore stomach lining after peptic ulcer. See Brussels Sprouts for more on the health power of crucifers.

VITAMIN & MINERAL

Vitamins – K, C, B6 (Pyridoxine), B1 (Thiamin), B2 (Riboflavin) and A
Minerals – Manganese, Calcium, Potassium and Magnesium

DISEASE PREVENTION

Reduces risk, symptoms and proliferation of cancer more than any other
fruits or vegetables in prostate, colon, lung, stomach, breast, ovaries and
bladder. Possibly occurs through increasing levels of isothiocyanate after
eating crucifers. A potent anti-cancer molecule that binds to toxins inducing their removal, stimulates cancer cell death, prevents excess cellular
dividing and promotes the healthy metabolism of hormones like estrogen.

HOW TO GROW

Cabbages come in dense versions, with green, red and purple heads, and
loose leaf versions including bok choy. Can be harvested all year long in
a mild climate with moist winters. Three divisions among varieties based
on harvest time: spring, summer and fall/winter. For spring cabbages, sow
seeds in seed beds with shallow drills spaced 6 inches apart in mid- to late
summer. Don't make the drills very long, as you only need 1.5 feet to produce 60-90 plants. Plant them out beginning early fall. Spring cabbages
grow in moderate climates only. For summer cabbages, sow seeds in trays
near the end of winter. These need to be transplanted indoors into a bigger container and kept under light or in a greenhouse. Or you may wait
longer and sow them outdoors in the spring when air and ground temperatures rise. For autumn/winter cabbages, which include red cabbage,
sow seeds in a bed with shallow drills in mid- to late spring with the same
spacing as spring cabbages. For all varieties, transplant when seedlings
have grown roughly 3 inches. Soften the seed bed with water the evening
before. Fill a small dirt hole with water and soak the seedling roots until
they are covered in muddy water. Plant each seedling in holes 6 inches
deep and 18 inches apart in rows spaced out 18 inches as well. Keep weed-
free and watered. Harvest when hearts feel solid. Cut at the base of stems.
You can preserve some varieties in a cool shed hung upside down.

INSECT CONTROL

See Brussels Sprouts for how to rid pests.

TIPS

Spring cabbages need a handful of fertilizer per plant in late winter to
keep them growing. Cook lightly to retain more phytonutrients. Choose
organic varieties, which have more phytonutrients that reduce cancer risk.

Cacti

HEALTH POWER ✛ Nopales (pads of prickly pear cactus) are especially good for cardiovascular, colon and immune system health. Rich in vitamins A and C, both potent antioxidants that protect cells/tissues from free radical damage that leads to DNA mutations. Also preserve elasticity and integrity of blood cell walls and other epithelial tissues. Help reduce inflammations linked to arthritis or asthma. Rich in phytonutrients called flavonoids, also powerful antioxidants. Soluble and insoluble fibers aid digestion, lower blood glucose, cholesterol and triglycerides. Fiber, antioxidants and other phytonutrients work synergistically to combat oxidative stress, optimize immune function, maintain good systemic balance and help prevent adverse conditions.

VITAMIN & MINERAL ⬆ Vitamins – A, C, K, B6 (Pyridoxine) and B2 (Riboflavin)
Minerals – Manganese, Calcium, Magnesium and Potassium

DISEASE PREVENTION ⊘ Reduces symptoms or risk of constipation, gastric ulcers, atherosclerosis, heart disease, diabetes, breast cancer and colon cancer.

HOW TO GROW ও Several thousand species of cacti grow in the U.S., but only about 100 can grow outside arid regions of the Southwest. Prickly pears of the genus Opuntia are most common in northern areas, being hardy down to minus 40°F. Most cacti produce gorgeous flowers in spring; some even produce edible fruit or vegetables. Opuntia ficus-indica produces fig-shaped fruit (prickly pears) about 2 inches long, as sweet as peaches. Pads of this species, nopales, are edible. Others popular in China and Vietnam produce pitaya, also known as dragon fruit. Consult local nursery for which cultivar grows best in your area. Cacti require full sun (minimum 6 hours per day) and excellent drainage for optimum growth. Work in a generous amount of compost or planting mix rich in organic matter. Add coarse sand, gravel and some limestone. If soil naturally retains much water, create a raised bed. Plant in spring but plan for the function and mature size of cactus. Prickly pears spread about 2 feet, others more confined, some grow wider. Check with nursery before planting. Protect hands with gloves, or even magazine, newspaper or cardboard, from both visible spines and smaller, hooked spines called glochids. Post planting, put a layer of gravel around base to prevent rot. Little maintenance required. Apply liquid fertilizer or other micronutrient-rich mix each spring. When harvesting prickly pears from Opuntia ficus-indica, handle with care; tiny glochids hard to remove if wedged in skin. Can grow in containers indoors, but less than full potential with lack of sunlight.

| INSECT CONTROL | ✗ | Tough, almost impenetrable, texture and sharp spines protect cacti from pests. |

| TIPS | ✓ | Be careful while harvesting. Use gloves. Soaking prickly pears in scalding water for a few minutes makes peeling skin containing glochids much easier. |

Carrots

| HEALTH POWER | + | Many health benefits. Great source of antioxidant compounds. Rank among highest carotenoid contents. Help regulate blood sugar levels and reduce insulin resistance, a common cause of diabetes. High vitamin A helps eyes adjust to changing brightness and promotes good night vision. Vitamin A reduces risk of emphysema from exposure to cigarette smoke. |

| VITAMIN & MINERAL | ↑ | Vitamins – A, K, C, B6 (Pyridoxine), B1 (Thiamin), B3 (Niacin), B9 (Folate)
Minerals – Potassium, Manganese, Molybdenum, Phosphorus and Magnesium |

| DISEASE PREVENTION | ⊘ | One daily serving of carrots or squash cuts in half risk of heart disease among elderly. Beta-carotene from carrots converts to Vitamin A in liver; travels to eye where it helps produce chemicals needed for night vision. Beta-carotene has antioxidant properties that help prevent cataracts and macular degeneration. High levels of carotenoids with falcarinol defend against many cancers: postmenopausal breast, bladder, cervix, prostate, larynx, esophagus, colon and lung. Carotenoids in carrots may work only when grouped into biochemical team, since supplementation of only one carotenoid, beta-carotene, is not as effective. |

HOW TO GROW

Easy to grow with quality soil. Varieties differ in maturation timing and size. Plant in less dense, finer soil. Need well-aged compost or mature organic matter to grow well. (Fresh manure or compost causes deformed root growth and atypical tastes.) Lacking light soil, grow in raised deep beds. Some smaller types will grow in shallower soil, but larger crop demands deep raised beds or deep sandy loam soil. To create a deep raised bed, dig a trench of desired width and one spade deep. Break up the bottom soil layer to create room for roots to explore. Mix in couple inches of well-aged, disease-free manure, compost or planting mix. Fill trench half way and add another couple inches. Finish by filling the trench with the remainder of the soil dug up. For good measure, throw over the top a few handfuls of planting mix containing alfalfa, fish bone or kelp meal. Needs pH near 6.5; add lime to raise. Sow seeds directly into permanent rows in late winter for warm climates and mid-spring in cooler areas. Place a pinch or about 5-6 seeds per inch of the row. Cover the row with a thin layer of topsoil (roughly ½ inch or slightly more in dry areas). Water softly, but keep seeds moist so they germinate and sprout in 1-3 weeks. When tops reach a few inches high, mulch around plants to help retain moisture. Ready for harvest when big enough to eat. Moisten soil to make it easier to pull out.

INSECT CONTROL

Carrots usually problem free. Common pests include carrot fly, parsley worms and nematodes. Biggest threats are gophers, deer, woodchucks and rabbits. If these are large risk, erect large barriers or fences to block entry. Block gophers with underground fence or flood them out of their holes. Interplant with onions to repel carrot flies or cover rows with plastic lining. Crop rotation helps prevent nematode infestation. Plant marigolds year before to remove them from soil.

TIPS

Crowded carrots interfere with each other and grow deformed. When the sprouts are 2-3 inches high, thin the rows so plants are separated by 1 inch. Repeat in several weeks to make them 4 inches apart. Carrots respond well to container planting if you want to grow just a few carrots and avoid effort of creating deeper bed of lighter soil.

Cauliflower

HEALTH POWER

Like other crucifers, cauliflower contains glucosinolates (sulforaphane) and thiocyanates (isothiocyanate). Together, they increase the ability of liver cells to create compounds that remove harmful, sometimes cancer-causing, toxins. See Brussels Sprouts and Cabbage for more on the detoxification benefits of eating crucifers. Cauliflower itself also contains enzymes that assist in detoxification. Cauliflower also provides dietary fiber and the B vitamin folate. Fiber promotes healthy digestion and lower blood cholesterol levels. Pregnant women need folate to ensure the healthy development of their baby's nervous system.

VITAMIN & MINERAL

Vitamins – C, K, B6 (Pyridoxine), B5 (Pantothenic Acid), B2 (Riboflavin), B1 (Thiamin) and B3 (Niacin)
Minerals – Manganese, Potassium, Phosphorus and Magnesium

DISEASE PREVENTION

Eating cruciferous vegetables several times a week reduces the risk of many cancers, sometimes by up to 50 percent. Such cancers include lung, colon, breast, ovary, bladder, colorectal and prostate. Research has found the spice turmeric has a compound, curcumin, that, with the many isothiocyanates in crucifers, may retard or inhibit the growth of prostate cancer cells. Middle-aged men concerned about prostate enlargement may do well by regularly eating cauliflower with turmeric. Cauliflower may also protect from cardiovascular disease, arthritis, and indigestion.

HOW TO GROW

Cauliflowers are the most difficult crucifer/brassica to grow due to their sensitivity to nutrient deficiencies and club root disease. Try to grow these only if your land is free of club root. Like cabbage, cauliflower comes in three types: summer, fall and winter/spring. Choose a site with full sun. Amend the soil with plenty of organic matter from a planting mix, aged manure or compost. Cauliflower must have access to all the micronutrients for proper growth. Make the pH 6.5-7. Add lime to raise, if needed. For summer varieties, sow seeds in mid-winter in a tray on a windowsill or in a greenhouse. Transplant into bigger seed trays when large enough to handle so they do not go hungry. Plant them out as soon as they reach 2 inches tall into spaces 18-22 inches square. Consider planting under cloches to protect from cold and pests. You can successively sow seeds on a windowsill in late winter and outdoors in shallow drills throughout spring for a continuous harvest. Autumn cauliflowers are the most popular. For them, sow seeds mid-spring in shallow drills separated by 5-7 inches. Plant out in early to mid-summer in holes as deep as they were, making sure to space them out about 24 inches square. For winter/spring varieties, sow seeds in mid- to late spring. Transplant into spaces 30 inches square when they reach 3 inches tall. Keep the area weed free. Cover soil around the plants with organic matter or plastic to retain moisture. Keep watered, as they wither quickly. Cut the curds as they develop into proper sizes. If too many of the summer types are ready at the same time, cut them and store in a cool shed. Remove stumps after harvesting and dispose or compost them. Leave the fall and winter/spring types to harvest when ready to eat to avoid their running to seed.

INSECT CONTROL ✗ Cauliflowers are bothered by a number of common pests. See Brussels Sprouts and Broccoli for common treatments. Your rapid response to infestation or disease is crucial with cauliflower to avoid compromising the crop by premature curding.

TIPS ✓ Keep micronutrients available for cauliflower, as deficiencies cause deformities. Fertilizing with a nutrient-dense fertilizer (such as alfalfa, fish bone or kelp meal) halfway through growth may help avoid potential problems with soils bordering on deficient. For fall cauliflowers, compact the soil around the base to provide support. For winter/spring varieties, angle the plants away from the morning sun to prevent the middle curds from thawing out too quickly, which can ruin flavor and change the color. Keep the curds out of direct sunlight by bending over a large leaf to cover them. Also, spray stored cauliflowers with water to keep them happy.

Celery

HEALTH POWER + Excellent source of Vitamin C, antioxidant that fights free radicals and plaque build up in blood vessels. Phthalides linked with lowered blood pressure by helping arteries dilate. Lowers cholesterol. Diuretic helps get rid of excess fluids. Promotes overall health and optimizes function of immune and vascular systems.

VITAMIN & MINERAL

Vitamins – K, C, B6 (Pyridoxine), B1 (Thiamin), A and B2 (Riboflavin)
Minerals – Potassium, Folate, Molybdenum, Manganese, Calcium, Magnesium, Phosphorus and Iron

DISEASE PREVENTION

Celery contains many antioxidants including coumarins that decrease the build up of cancer precursors and promote white blood cell activity. Acetylenics also stop cancer cell growth.

HOW TO GROW

Two types of celery, self blanching and blanched. Prefer areas where growing seasons are long, moist and cool but not frosting. Choose site with minimum 6 hours daily sunlight. Requires soil that easily retains moisture; digging in organic matter is a must. Get started celery plants at nursery. If you begin from seed, start indoors 6-8 weeks before last frost. Celery likes soil pH near 6.5. Add lime to bring toward neutral. Harden off seedlings and transplant to garden when temperatures are consistently above 50°F. With blanching celery, dig a small trench for optimum growth. Before transplanting, dig a trench one spade deep and long enough to space celery plants 12 inches apart. Place a shallow layer of compost, manure and/or plant mix in bottom. Cover organics with thin film of soil. Plant seedlings one foot apart and wrap stems with cardboard or a semi-resilient material. Keep soil saturated and feed animal manure liquid fertilizer or sprinkle another organic fertilizer on half-way through growing season. Mid-season and in one month intervals, fill trench with soil up to bottom of leaves. This is the blanching process. For self-blanching types, plant on flat ground in organic-rich soil. For both, keep soil moist and weed free.

INSECT CONTROL

Susceptible to slugs, celery fly and celery leaf. See Artichokes for anti-slug treatments. Celery fly causes leaves to turn pale green, then brown and shriveled. Remove affected leaves and destroy immediately. Celery leaf spots are brown spots on leaves and stems caused by fungus. Immune seeds available are treated with non-organic fungicide. For natural treatment, remove affected leaves and spray every two weeks with Bordeaux mixture until two weeks before harvest.

TIPS

Harvest self-blanching celery before the first frost. Use blanched types from first frost until well into winter. Use Golden-self blanching plants. If blanching yourself, do not let soil pack against the stems, which can cause rot.

Chamomile

Before modern medicine, herbal treatments were popular way to soothe ailments. Some of chamomile's powers discovered long ago still used effectively. Brewed tea from chamomile flowers is calming. Some say chamomile helps reduce nervousness, minor insomnia and aids digestion and upset stomachs. Essential oil from flowers gives more concentrated dose in a cup of tea. Oil obtained through steam distillation. Usually found at herb shops or some grocery stores. Blue color comes from the phytonutrient azulene, which has anti-inflammatory properties. Oil can be used to reduce skin conditions like rashes or eczema, help aid digestion and PMS symptoms. You may also enjoy the fragrance of dried flowers or soothe skin ailments (sunburn and others) by putting dried flowers in a permeable sack to soak in bath water.

Vitamins – traces of B1 (Thiamin), B2 (Riboflavin), A and B9 (Folate)
Minerals – Manganese and traces of Copper, Iron, Magnesium, Potassium & Zinc

May help soothe symptoms of skin conditions eczema, psoriasis, sunburns and rashes. May also help with indigestion. Often used to help reduce infant crying (colic) from teething pain, anxiety and insomnia.

Different varieties of chamomile available. Some perennial, others annual. Some used as ground cover or bordering. German variety is an annual used to make tea, as is the Roman perennial. Needs well-drained soil. Prefers site with partial shade, but can tolerate full sun. Can be grown in smaller areas, but may need to be kept in check later to keep from spreading. Growing in pots also an option. Work in compost or planting mix rich in organic matter/microbes into the soil of desired location. Start from seed or plant transplants from reputable nursery. In spring or mid-fall (in warmer climates), plant about 1.5 feet apart if growing for herb use or 8 inches apart for ground cover. Once they are a few inches tall, mulch around with fine fertile material that will not disrupt pH or block water absorption. Don't use pine bark or peat. Water just enough to keep soil moist. Trim off faded or dying flowers/leaves to promote new blooms. Chamomile peaks early through mid-summer with yellow and white flowers. Remove these to make tea. When frost comes, remove annuals and cut back perennials to just a few inches. To over winter perennials, insulate with a layer of mulch.

INSECT CONTROL ✕ No pest or disease problems if grown in open position with sun and wind, especially if a number of plants are grown.

TIPS ✓ Chamomile thrives best in areas where summer temperatures stay below 100°F. Be careful using chamomile as an herbal remedy. If you are allergic to daisy or ragweed, you may have an allergic reaction to chamomile. Also has blood-thinning action. Discuss with your doctor if you take prescription blood thinner.

Cherries

HEALTH POWER + Red color of this tasty treat comes from the powerful antioxidants known as anthocyanins. Cherries packed with free radical destroyers; almost as many as blueberries. Help with pain of inflammatory conditions like arthritis and muscle soreness. Linked with heart benefits by reducing inflammation and total cholesterol, and lowering body fat and total weight. Low in fat, high in water content and helps boost metabolism. One of only a few foods with melatonin. (Produced in pineal gland and associated with sleep rhythms. Cherries may help you get to sleep.) The high potassium content also can help control blood pressure and maintain proper muscle and nerve cell functioning.

VITAMIN & MINERAL ⬆ Vitamins – A, C, B2 (Riboflavin), B6 (Pyridoxine), B9 (Folate) and K
Minerals – Iron, Copper, Manganese, Potassium and Magnesium

DISEASE PREVENTION ⊘ The flavonoids (anthocyanins and quercetin) as well as the phenolic acid amygdalin in cherries may help lower symptoms or onset of several conditions: heart disease, pain from rheumatoid arthritis and gout, diabetes and other connective tissue ailments. Some studies show a reduced risk for colon and breast cancer by controlling cell-damaging free radicals.

HOW TO GROW

A tasty addition to the garden. Grow well in moderately cool temperatures but not constantly freezing. Many varieties self-pollinate. Must match the cultivar to your area. Consult trusted fruit tree supplier for one that grows well and matches your taste. Varieties are sweet, sour, dwarf and standard. Pick site with plenty of sunlight. Thrive in soil rich in nutrients and organic matter. Soil should be pH 6-8 with moisture retentive, well-drained loam. Prepare soil area of five square feet by adding generous amounts of organic matter and nutrient rich planting mix or well-aged compost. Rock dusts also good to work in, because they continue to release vital nutrients for years. One-year-old trees are best to start. Make sure to allow for space of branches and foliage, usually just over 20 feet in diameter for full-size tree. Dig the hole 6 inches to a foot wider and deeper than the ball of roots in the transplant. Loosen soil at bottom of hole by poking with pitchfork or similar tool. Cut off elongated roots with a clean tool, plant tree and firm in soil around roots. Water until air bubbles stop appearing. Prune tree/s back to around 2-3 feet by cutting slightly above connection to an adjacent branch. Decreasing demand for water and nutrients will buy time for roots to catch up with supply. Shape as desired. Most importantly, cut internal lateral branches close to the trunk to maintain room for air and sun. Other than that, leave them to grow or trim branches similar to peach trees to increase fruit size. Leave cherries on tree as long as you can, but pick before they split. Eat sweet cherries right away. Use tart ones to cook with, bottle or make into jam within a few days.

INSECT CONTROL

Birds are main threat to cherries. Plan on losing about 30 percent of crop. If planting only one tree, consider planting a mulberry tree nearby to distract birds from cherries. They love mulberries. (If growing more than one tree, you will have more fruit than one family can think of consuming per season.) Sometimes aphids, winter moth or bacterial canker cause problems. Spray off aphids with a strong stream. Best way to get rid of winter moths: secure a grease band around the tree between fall and spring to stop females from crawling up to lay eggs. To rid bacterial canker, cut and dispose of all infected wood. Then spray copper fungicide three times with one month between applications.

TIPS

When planting in windy, more exposed locations, support tree with a stake until trunk and roots are strong enough.

Chives

HEALTH POWER +

Provide only small amounts of vitamins, minerals and phytonutrients (from garnishing dishes with chives), but they add to the overall health of meals. High vitamin K, A and C content by weight. Vitamins A and C have antioxidant properties that help rid body of damaging free radicals. Vitamin K helps build bone and form blood clots. Some suggest they have antibiotic action, aid digestion, improve blood flow and stimulate appetite. Research still young on this member of the onion family, but more study may reveal potentially great benefits.

VITAMIN & MINERAL ↑

Vitamins – K, A, C and B9 (Folate)
Minerals – Manganese

DISEASE PREVENTION ⊘

Much more research needed. Thus far, researchers say eating chives regularly may reduce risk of prostate cancer. Chives may be as beneficial as its cousins in the Allium family (onions, garlic, leeks, shallots and scallions).

HOW TO GROW

A great addition to the garden. Useful as ornamental piece along borders or inside garden. Nice flower blooms. Take well to containers, too. Hardy perennial herb tolerant of both sun and shade. Only soil preference is keep it moist. The pH can vary and chives will still thrive. Sow seeds in early spring spaced 12 inches apart. Or separate already-developed plants and replant 12 inches apart in early spring or fall. Keep them watered and watch them grow. Every three years or so, dig up the groups, divide in half, and replant in fresh soil. If you don't want to move, dig them up and plant temporarily in a pot or unused section of soil. Rework the original soil and amend with compost or planting mix. Then replant back in for another few years. Chives are stimulated to re-grow quickly when cut, so cut down to about half inch above ground as needed. Remove weeds as soon as noticed. Or lay down layer of mulch.

INSECT CONTROL ✕

No specific or common pests that damage them. If problem occurs, consult local nursery for treatment.

TIPS ✓

Chives store well frozen, but not as well as dry herbs. Lose much of their flavor when stored. If they become woody, trim down to about an inch above ground.

Cilantro

HEALTH POWER

Cilantro leaves and coriander seeds both packed with beneficial phyto-nutrients. Animal research shows promising health benefits for humans. Regularly eating coriander may reduce bad cholesterol levels (the LDL form), control blood sugar by stimulating insulin production in pancreatic cells and reduce cellular damage by free radicals. Coriander contributes fiber that promotes healthy digestion and nutrient extraction from foods. Coriander has antibiotic components. The volatile oil dodecenal kills Salmonella bacteria responsible for many food poisonings. Cilantro helps remove potentially toxic heavy metals that damage nerve functions. Many popular antioxidants help defend important cells from damage that could lead to reduced vision, higher cholesterol, weakened blood vessels and minor inflammation.

VITAMIN & MINERAL

Vitamins – traces
Minerals – Manganese, Iron and Magnesium

DISEASE PREVENTION

Cilantro in the regular diet may help reduce symptoms or even prevent heart disease, arthritis, Alzheimer's and anemia. Cilantro has also been a popular treatment to help defend against urinary tract infections.

HOW TO GROW

Cilantro is an annual plant with very aromatic leaves. Also known as the producer of coriander seeds, it grows easily in a container or on the plant bed in a garden. Grows best in sheltered, rich, moist and well-drained soil in full sun. If you get extreme heat, consider a site shaded part of the day. Difficult to transplant. If growing outdoors, plant seeds in spring after the last frost. Weeds tend to grow faster at first than your herb, so keep them weed free early on. Plant seeds half inch deep and spaced out about an inch. If growing in rows, keep rows 12-15 inches apart. Begin to harvest leaves when the plant is roughly 6 inches tall. Harvest outside leaves first, and thin out the plant as you go to maintain good air circulation. For maximum leaf production, cut off the flower stalks when they develop, which forces more energy into leaf production. When the plant bolts to seed, collect seeds and use them as a spice or a way to get more cilantro later on. Cilantro loses its flavor quickly when it dries out, so keep it fresh in a cool area.

Cilantro's pungent smell keeps most pests away. If any, aphids or white flies might attack. Aphids can be expelled with a strong stream of water, but cilantro is too weak to withstand it. Instead, destroy aphids, (which attack many plants) by planting French marigolds to attract their predators. Hoverflies and ladybugs eat aphids by the thousands. White flies are strongly attracted to the color yellow. Get rid of them by creating an old fashioned flytrap with yellow paper and a gooey substance to cover the paper. White flies will land on the paper and be stuck for good.

Another way to experiment with the initial planting is to start a few indoors and transplant them outside after the last frost while also planting seeds directly outdoors. Get a continuous sowing of seeds going in the spring for continuous harvest, because cilantro runs to seed rather quickly after sprouting up.

Collards

Collard greens are nutritional rock stars loaded with beneficial phytonutrients, vitamins and minerals. Rich in antioxidants, B vitamins and important minerals. An excellent choice for heart health. Sulfurous phytonutrients (glucosinolates and cysteine sulfoxides) inhibit growth of many types of cancers. Some stimulate liver to produce detoxification enzymes that work synergistically to speed up removing free radicals and toxins. Vitamins and minerals promote cardiovascular, immune system, brain and overall health through direct interactions and antioxidant effects. Provide antioxidant vitamins A, C and E. Vitamin C protects water-soluble areas (inside and outside of cells). Vitamins A and E protect fatty molecules and structures, together protecting cell machinery (proteins, enzymes, cell membranes, DNA, mitochondria). Free radicals oxidize cholesterol, which converts to a form that sticks to blood vessel walls (initiating plaque buildup). Vitamin A and zinc help maintain healthy epithelial cells (skin, mucus membranes, gastrointestinal tract, vaginal epithelium), the first line of defense against infection. Folate and other B vitamins moderate homocysteine level in blood by converting to safe form. Potassium and magnesium help reduce elevated blood pressure. Manganese is enzyme cofactor (activator) and integral part of enzymes that make vitamin C useable. Also facilitates antioxidant superoxide dismutase, protecting mitochondria from free radical byproducts. Calcium, essential for healthy bone, also helps prevent menopausal bone loss, migraines, PMS symptoms and helps protect colon cells from carcinogens. Dietary fiber promotes smooth, healthy digestion, helps regulate blood sugar and lowers elevated cholesterol.

VITAMIN & MINERAL ⬆

Vitamins – K, A, C, E, B9 (Folate), B6 (Pyridoxine), B2 (Riboflavin), B3 (Niacin), B1 (Thiamin) and B5 (Pantothenic Acid)
Minerals – Manganese, Calcium, Potassium, Magnesium, Zinc and Iron

DISEASE PREVENTION 🚫

Collards may provide risk reduction or symptom relief for atherosclerosis, heart disease, osteoarthritis, macular degeneration, osteoporosis, diabetes, and cancers of lung, breast, ovary, prostate and colon.

HOW TO GROW 🌱

Very popular Southern vegetable, yet grow well in cooler regions, too. These crucifers are cold hardy, similar to kale and cabbage. See Kale for site, soil and maintenance needs. Spring usually best time for planting. Plant seeds ¼ inch deep a few weeks before last frost. When seedlings emerge, space them 1 foot apart in rows 3 feet apart. For fall harvest, plant seeds 2-2.5 months before the first frost. Collards slower to mature than kale (70-80 days). Keep soil moist. Collards like foliar feeding. Apply liquid fertilizer a few times during growth season and spread out evenly. Leaves ready to harvest when the plant is about 1 foot tall. Pick outer leaves first.

INSECT CONTROL ✕

See Cabbage and Kale for pest control methods.

TIPS ✓

Flavor is better after cool weather, especially right after frost.

Corn

HEALTH POWER ✚

More than just a source of starch and carbohydrates. Corn contributes to heart health, lung health, energy production, metabolism and memory. Yellow corn higher in carotene lutein than white corn, hence yellow color. Lutein great for eyes. B vitamin folate helps prevent birth defects and lowers homocysteine in blood, a molecule linked to cardiovascular problems. Phytonutrient beta-cryptoxanthin found in corn (also oranges and red bell peppers) may protect lungs from carcinogens. B vitamin pantothenic acid helps maintain energy by breaking down carbohydrates, fats and proteins. Thiamin helps provide energy and contributes to brain health by helping synthesize acetylcholine, a crucial neurotransmitter for memory and neural function in general. Fiber aids healthy digestion and lowers total cholesterol. Whole grain foods like corn and wheat are rich in antioxidant phenolics, which work in synergy to help deal with adversity and prevent many diseases.

VITAMIN & MINERAL

Vitamins – B1 (Thiamin), B9 (Folate), C and B5 (Pantothenic Acid)
Minerals – Phosphorus and Manganese

DISEASE PREVENTION

Research incomplete on corn's antioxidant activity and general potential to prevent disease. Nutrients are linked with lower risks of heart disease, colon cancer, lung cancer, macular degeneration and Alzheimer's disease.

HOW TO GROW

Among oldest, most widespread foods. Grows in warm weather. Young corn very sensitive to frost and transplants. Start outdoors after soil warms up. To start earlier, use peat pots so roots are undisturbed when transplanting. Choose plot with full sun in area where they will not shade other crops that need sun. Amend soil well with aged compost or very fertile plant mix. Corn prefers slightly acidic pH. If below 5.5, add lime or dolomite to raise. Pollinated by wind, so plant in rectangles with rows close together. To ensure good pollination, plant 6 or more rows together in a group. Plant seeds outdoors (two in every one-inch deep hole) when temperature rises above 70°F. Space holes 8-12 inches. Cover holes with soil and compress a bit. Water thoroughly. Seeds will start showing after week one of watering. Keep weeds away, especially while plants are young. Cover surrounding area with mulch. Water regularly, especially on hot days. Corn is fully-grown and ready to harvest in about 3 months, when the top hairs turn brownish and kernels are plump.

INSECT CONTROL

Corn grown in highly fertile soil usually has few problems. Most common pests are flea beetles, earworms, cutworms and corn borers. Flea beetles are most damaging to young crops by chewing many small holes in leaves. Apply parasitic nematodes to soil. In extreme cases, spray with insecticide like rotenone. Corn borers enter the stalk below the tassel. Look for sawdust-like material next to small holes. Squeeze stalk to kill pest. Earworms feed on ear tips when little hairs emerge from the tips forming tassels. Look for them then and dispose. Cutworms chew on plant base just under surface. Attract ground beetles to eat them by growing ground cover nearby. Dig up area surrounding plant and hand pick or use cutworm collars on transplants.

TIPS ✓ Birds and raccoons can also be a problem during seed sowing and harvest. Aside from installing row covers, deter birds by getting rid of standing water, planting mulberry trees to distract them, removing trash and introducing an owl/scarecrow. A barrier (like taping ears to the stalk), night lighting or electric fencing will deter raccoons.

Cucumber

HEALTH POWER + Cucumbers contain silica, a trace mineral, which we need for healthy connective tissue (bone, ligaments, tendons, cartilage and muscle). Silica also encourages healthy skin. Some use it topically for swelling under the eyes, dermatitis and soothing sunburn. Cucumbers are 95 percent water by weight, so eating is a good way to hydrate. Cucumber adds some fiber to the diet, aiding digestion. With vitamins A and C, cucumber helps the immune system and the liver disarm free radicals that cause cellular damage.

VITAMIN & MINERAL ⬆ Vitamins – C, A and B9 (Folate)
Minerals – Molybdenum, Potassium, Manganese and Magnesium

DISEASE PREVENTION 🚫 With lower nutrient concentrations, cucumbers are good, but not major, contributors. The magnesium, potassium and fiber may help reduce hypertension. The fiber and water helps avoid indigestion.

HOW TO GROW  Cucumbers grow best in a sunny spot with rich soil. Amend the site with lots of compost or planting mix to achieve a pH close to 6. Sow seeds twice in the year for two harvests. The first one is in small pots indoors in early spring. Place two seeds to a pot at least 3 inches in diameter. Thin down to the strongest seedling if crowding occurs. Keep in a sunny location with moist soil. They should be ready to plant in late spring. Place about 2 feet apart. Make another sowing outdoors about 2 feet apart. If still cold in your area, put cutoff plastic bottles over the sowings to protect from night cold. You can grow cucumbers on the ground or up along sticks. Making a thin tepee with strong sticks looks cool, and it also keeps cucumbers off the ground and reduces their risk for disease, rot or slug infestation. If you plant them in the ground, space them out a little more than 2 feet, as they will grow out like vines. To keep them attached to the sticks as they grow, regularly tie them to the sticks with thick string. When the seedlings are about a foot tall, mulch with some organic matter. Also, trim back the side shoots to encourage growth upward. Pinch the tops of cucumber plants when they reach the top of the tepee. Keep soil moist. Starting roughly half way through growing season, begin fertilizing every few weeks. To produce more cucumbers, harvest cucumbers when young and plant still contains blooms. Failing this, entire plant stops producing.

INSECT CONTROL ✕ Popular pests of the cucumber bush include slugs, aphids, and cucumber beetles. To deter slugs, embed a cup of beer in the soil. Slugs and snails fall in and drown. If the plant is big enough and aphids are infesting, spray them off with a strong stream of water. Otherwise, plant French marigolds to attract their predators (hover flies, ladybugs). Inspect all plants and handpick any cucumber beetles when you notice them. You can also wait until later in the season to plant when beetles are on the wane. If they are especially prevalent, you can place row covers over them or, as a last resort, spray with insecticide.

TIPS ✓ Cucumbers are mostly water, so letting the plant dry out is not an option. During dry weather, water deep into the soil.

Dandelion

HEALTH POWER + Is the weed with the yellow flower in your backyard nutritious? Yes. Dandelion greens are a great source of many vitamins and a good source of many minerals. One serving has five times the recommended daily dose of vitamin K. Essential for bone health by increasing ratio of bone matrix development to bone breakdown, especially in the presence of calcium. Antidote for coumarin poisoning (rodent poison) since coumarins block liver production of vitamin K and cause internal bleeding. Greens loaded with antioxidant vitamins A and C, preventing buildup of harmful free radicals in water soluble areas of the body and promoting healthy cardiovascular function. Maintain elasticity in blood vessels and assist in blocking biochemical pathways that lead to plaque buildup. Potassium aids blood pressure by helping blood vessels relax. Enhance liver function, eyesight, immune system function and synthesis of connective tissue. Riboflavin and small amounts of other B vitamins assist in metabolism of carbohydrates, lipids and protein to provide energy or help develop body structure. Diuretic components cause kidneys to produce more urine, removing excess toxins, lowering high blood sugar and lowering blood pressure.

VITAMIN & MINERAL

Vitamins – K, A, C, E and B (Riboflavin)
Minerals – Calcium, Iron, Manganese, Potassium, Magnesium and Copper

DISEASE PREVENTION

High content of vitamins and minerals may help delay or prevent heart disease, atherosclerosis, rheumatoid and osteoarthritis, osteoporosis and cell damage leading to many types of cancer.

HOW TO GROW

We know it as a common weed, but dandelions have an attractive flower. Very tolerant and grow in most soils. If growing to eat, increase nutrition by selecting sunny site, amend soil with compost or planting mix and check drainage. Sow seeds in spring; water during dry weather. Thin out to 6 inches or more between plants to reduce disease risk and provide room for leaf growth. Harvest leaves like other leafy lettuce before they flower and/or go to seed, which leads to bitter taste.

INSECT CONTROL

No common pests for dandelions. Usually dandelion is the pest by growing as weed interfering with other plants. Strong taproot makes them hard to remove, which requires completely digging up roots without breaking off.

TIPS

When gone to seed, they spread rapidly and germinate. Alternative approach: grow in container to prevent spreading to undesired locations. Many highly nutritious juices and teas come from dandelion. Give them a try.

Dill

HEALTH POWER

The significant health benefits of dill come from unique phytonutrients, including monoterpenes (carvone, anethofuran, and limonene) and flavonoids (kaempferol and vicenin). Monoterpenes activate the antioxidant enzyme glutathione-S-transferase, which marks dangerous free radicals for destruction by other compounds. Dill's volatile oil has anti-bacterial properties. Like garlic and thyme, dill inhibits the growth of many common bacteria. Dill is also a great addition to dishes for its mineral and fiber content. A good source of calcium, dill contributes to bone maintenance. Its iron helps blood deliver oxygen to tissues. Fiber promotes smooth digestion and absorption of nutrients. Munching on dill seed has been used to stop hiccups. Making tea with dill is a popular cure for indigestion.

VITAMIN & MINERAL

Vitamins – traces
Minerals – Iron, Manganese and Calcium

DISEASE PREVENTION

In the small quantity dill is eaten, it does not significantly reduce disease risks. But added to dishes it helps prevent infection by pathogenic bacteria and bone loss (osteoporosis).

HOW TO GROW

Dill is an attractive, fast-growing annual herb native to the tropics. Many consider its taste a perfect complement to fish. The seeds are also used for flavoring pickles. The pleasant yellow flowers make a great plant for bordering. Dill plants prefer sunlight and well-drained soil. Plant in the spring. Amend the soil with compost or planting mix. Sow the seeds directly in the bed outdoors after the last frost when the soil begins to warm up. Thinly place the seeds in small rows spaced about 1 foot apart. Later thin the seedlings to 1 foot apart. If growing for the leaves, make successive sowings every month from mid-summer. Dill grows well in pots, too. Space them out 1 foot apart in pots. Avoid planting near their kin, fennel, as they may cross pollinate. Keep weed-free. Water enough to keep soil moist. Pick leaves fresh as needed. Or dry and collect leaves and seeds. If drying leaves, harvest the plant young before it flowers. Tie stems together in small bunches and hang upside down in a shady, well-ventilated area. If collecting seeds, cut just as seeds ripen, then hang upside down in small bunches in a dry, shady, well-ventilated area.

INSECT CONTROL ✕ No pest issues. Often used to attract beneficial insects in companion planting, including parasitic wasps and pollinating bees. Plant this herb near fruits and vegetables to help control pests and attract pollinators to get generous yields. If planted near tomatoes, dill strongly attracts hornworms, which are easier to spot and remove from dill.

TIPS ✓ Difficult to grow from transplants. Another way to collect seeds: Remove the whole flower head when the seed pods turn brown, place them in a paper bag and shake carefully. Seeds will fall out, and you can separate them from other plant matter.

Eggplant

HEALTH POWER + Eggplant has a nice mixture of vitamins, minerals and phytonutrients. Many of the phytonutrients, like phenolic compounds and flavonoids, are antioxidants. One flavonoid, nasunin, protects the membranes around each cell. Especially important because cell membranes control traffic in and out of each cell, contain receptors for messenger compounds that tell the cell what to do and are the protective barrier between inside and outside. Among phenolic compounds, chlorogenic acid is a potent antioxidant in highest concentrations. With flavonoids, these compounds disarm free radicals in many locations to help stop oxidative cell damage (which could develop into cancer), help relax blood vessels, lower cholesterol and plaque buildup, help ward off microbes and viruses and reduce free-radical stress in joints, a primary part of arthritis development. Eggplant also has fiber, potassium and several B vitamins to help promote healthy metabolism, digestion and nerve/muscle function. All these benefits are low-cost, because eggplant is low in fat and sugar.

VITAMIN & MINERAL ↑ Vitamins – B1 (Thiamin), B6 (Pyridoxine), B9 (Folate) and B3 (Niacin) Minerals – Potassium, Manganese, Copper and Magnesium

DISEASE PREVENTION ⊘ Eggplant may help reduce risks for, or symptoms of, rheumatoid and osteoarthritis, heart disease, cancer cell development, type II diabetes and others.

HOW TO GROW

Eggplants are native to the tropics and do not produce through cold winters. Grown as annuals in cooler climates and perennials in warmer ones. Can be found as seeds or bought as young plants. An earlier variety will produce longer. Choose a sheltered site with full sun and well-drained soil. Amend the soil with aged compost, manure or planting mix. Grow best in soil with pH 6.5. If you live in a cooler region, you may need to warm up the soil by covering with black plastic weeks in advance. In cool climates, sow seeds indoors on a windowsill or under fluorescent light in early to mid-spring. A week or two before planting out, harden them off by bringing outdoors for increasing periods. In late spring, plant out 2 feet apart in rows underneath plastic row covers. In warmer climates, row covers not needed. Eggplants get bulky for stems to hold, so tie main stem to a stake in multiple places to provide weight support and keep them off the ground. Water when needed and monitor regularly to see how they grow. If they do not branch out from the main stem when they are 10 inches high, pinch out the growth tip. Also, limit fruits to about 5 per plant to ensure all get loaded with nutrients and grow in a healthy way. Remove extra flowers after about 5 have fruited and begun to develop. Treat soil each week with nutrient-dense liquid fertilizer like compost tea, manure tea or liquid seaweed. Begin harvesting eggplants in late summer when they are fully mature and shining.

INSECT CONTROL

Aphids, whitefly and red spider mite are common pests of eggplants. The spider mites thrive in dryness, so keep the plant moist by spraying regularly. Control aphids by planting French marigolds, which attract predators like hover flies and ladybugs that eat them by the thousands. White flies can be trapped in an old-style flytrap. They are attracted to the color yellow, so construct a trap by covering some yellow material with a sticky substance. Hang it near the plants at risk or under attack. Whiteflies fly into trap and get stuck in adhesive.

TIPS

Harvest before eggplants lose their shine or they will taste bitter.

Endive

HEALTH POWER

Endive is particularly rich in vitamin K, which is essential for several proteins that make blood clot. (The name K comes from the German word koagulation.) If blood does not clot, wounds bleed out of control. Vitamin K plays an important role in bone formation. Many foods contain vitamin K, and a deficiency is rare. Endive is also a good source of vitamin A, folate and fiber. Vitamin A is a fat-soluble antioxidant that clears destructive free radicals and helps maintain healthy epithelial tissue around blood vessels and organs such as the liver and stomach. Folate protects blood vessel walls from early damage that can lead to stroke and heart attack. Folate converts the molecule homocysteine into harmless molecules used for other purposes. Folate also helps with cell growth and normal fetal development, making it essential during pregnancy. It also aids digestion by stimulating alkaline bile, which may help balance intestinal pH like a mild antacid.

VITAMIN & MINERAL

Vitamins – K, A, B9 (Folate), C and B5 (Pantothenic Acid)
Minerals – Manganese, Potassium and Iron

DISEASE PREVENTION

Endive may reduce the risk of anemia and cancer in the rectum, skin and bladder. It may also help ward off atherosclerosis or other cardiovascular disease. Due to its alkaline nature, endive can reduce minor symptoms of heartburn or acid indigestion.

HOW TO GROW

Endive is a salad vegetable great for late summer or early fall harvest (winter in warmer climates). Flavor is bitter like chicory and can be tough if not cared for properly. Choose a partly shaded site to prevent excess bitterness and running to seed too soon. Prefers rich medium loam soil that holds moisture well with a pH near 6.5. Work in highly fertile compost or planting mix a couple weeks before sowing. For a fall and/or winter harvest, sow in midsummer and/or late summer, respectively. Place seeds in shallow drills roughly 1 foot apart. Direct sowing is the best way to plant, since transplanting causes endive to run to seed quickly. Keep soil moist and weed as needed to keep beds free of competition. The most-recently-sown rows may need cloche covers in cooler climates to prevent cold damage. About 12 weeks after sowing, blanch the endive to create a more delicate flavor. Do this by placing flowerpots over them. Cover the pothole in the bottom to block sunlight. Leave as is for a few weeks. Ready to harvest when hearts are a light creamy color.

INSECT CONTROL	✕	Generally pest free. If you get an infestation of anything, ask your local nursery what might cause problems in your area.
TIPS	✓	Toss mixed greens, sliced pear, candied walnuts, gorgonzola cheese and raspberry vinaigrette with endive for a tasty dinner appetizer.

Fennel

HEALTH POWER	+	Fennel has promising phytonutrients with potent antioxidant activity, anti-inflammatory properties, and the ability to inhibit cancer cell development (according to early research). Most notable is phytonutrient anethole. In animal studies, anethole reduced inflammation and blocked the initiation of cancer cells through the inhibition of one or more biochemical pathways. Fennel is a great way to get vitamin C, potassium, folate and fiber. Vitamin C is a versatile antioxidant. It protects cells in water-soluble areas from free radical damage that can lead to arthritis and atherosclerosis. It may also be needed by the immune system for optimum function against harmful invaders. Fiber, folate and potassium together are great for the digestive tract and cardiovascular system. Fiber helps the intestines and lowers elevated levels of cholesterol and blood sugar. Folate prevents the buildup of homocysteine in the blood, a compound known to cause vessel damage in high concentrations. Fennel has potassium as well, which promotes healthy nerve and muscle functions and helps lower blood pressure.
VITAMIN & MINERAL	⬆	Vitamins – C, B9 (Folate) and B3 (Niacin) Minerals – Potassium, Manganese, Molybdenum, Phosphorus, Calcium, Magnesium, Iron and Copper
DISEASE PREVENTION	🚫	Fennel may reduce symptoms or the onset of rheumatoid and osteoarthritis, cardiovascular disease, heart attack, stroke and colon cancer. High antioxidant activity (and the phytonutrient anethole) may reduce cell damage that causes many other types of cancer.
HOW TO GROW		You can grow fennel for its swollen base or leaves. It can reach a height of 5-6 feet tall. Varieties grown for stem bases are called Florence fennel.

Both types need sunny site with well-drained, living soil holding the right micronutrients and microbes. The pH should be above 6.5. To gain these optimal growing conditions, work in some compost and planting mix. Fennel is a perennial that can be planted in either spring or fall. Sow regular fennel seeds or plant young seedlings roughly 2 feet apart. If planting Florence fennel, sow seeds only in spring in shallow drills 1.5 feet apart. Later thin the seedlings to 8-10 inches apart. Keep plants weed free. Water when soil begins to dry. If Florence fennel dries out, it runs to seed and compromises the crop. Trim regular fennel plants down as they grow to promote continuous growth of fresh young leaves. Let some shoots produce flowers and go to seed for a stock. Make sure not to plant fennel next to other spices like dill, coriander or caraway as they can cross pollinate each other. Every few years, lift fennel and replant somewhere else so the soil can reach its original balance again. Harvest the leaves as needed. To get seeds, hang the flowers upside down in a dry area with a cloth underneath to catch them when they fall.

INSECT CONTROL ✗ Most fennel is not affected by pests. Florence fennel can be bothered by slugs and celery fly. To rid the garden of slugs, embed a glass of beer in the soil. The slugs will be attracted, slither into the cup and drown. Celery flies are tough to notice until they cause leaves to turn pale and then brown. Remove these leaves and destroy them away from the garden.

TIPS ✓ Many plants have trouble growing next to fennel, because its large taproot competes for nutrients. Best solution is to grow it at least 3 feet away from other plants.

Figs

HEALTH POWER + Figs are a great source of potassium, which supports healthy nerve function and muscle contraction. A diet with many potassium-rich fruits and vegetables is linked to lower blood pressure compared to diets with little potassium. Figs have little calcium, but their potassium helps decrease the amount of calcium lost in urine, which makes figs a net supporter of bone health. The dietary fiber promotes healthy digestion, regulates cholesterol and blood sugar levels, and may support weight loss. Research on the benefits of fig leaves suggests phytonutrients within the leaves can help lower the amount of insulin needed by dependent diabetics. They may also reduce triglycerides in blood and inhibit the growth of some cancers. Watch for future discoveries of the health benefits linked to fig trees.

VITAMIN & MINERAL

Vitamins – trace amounts
Minerals – Potassium and Manganese

DISEASE PREVENTION

Figs are linked to a lower risk of post-menopausal breast cancer. They also support bone health, perhaps forestalling osteoporosis. Heart healthy, they may reduce complications of high blood pressure.

HOW TO GROW

Figs are a cool, tasty little specialty fruit to have growing in the back yard. They can be trained as fan trees, bush trees or left alone to do what they will. Bush trees will grow roughly 10 feet high, fan trees 15 feet. Let the tree shape itself with some minor pruning. Figs need a sunny site and soil that holds moisture well but has good drainage for the excess. The pH should be around 7 or just below. If your garden area is small and you don't want to risk casting shade over other plants, grow the figs along a south wall so it gets full sun. If growing more than one tree, plant trees 12-15 feet apart. Choose a tree well adapted to your climate. Self-fertilizing trees are easier to grow. The local nursery should have a young transplant geared for your environment. Dig a deep hole and amend it with aged compost, planting mix or well-aged manure. Plant the fig in and fill the hole with the amended soil. Water manually during first year and during dry spells. In winter, prune out old wood. Thin out branches in summer so fruit can ripen in sun. Also, cut away any sucker sprouts that come up from roots during growth. Replant these or give away. Figs are ready to harvest when skin changes color. Dark skinned ones turn dark purple; light skinned turn yellow. Eat straight off tree or store by drying or freezing.

INSECT CONTROL

Figs rarely have serious pests. Sometimes birds, botrytis and canker can be a problem. If birds are a serious issue, the only sure way to protect the tree is to surround it with netting. You may also try planting a mulberry tree to divert them to what they love. Canker starts with eroding patches of bark that grow bigger. When you notice it, cut off the diseased patches or branches and dispose of them. Botrytis is gray mold that thrives in cold, moist conditions. To avoid Botrytis, make sure the tree has good air circulation, drainage and no excess water. Remove infected growth and destroy immediately.

TIPS ✓ If fruit yield is your top priority, restrict root growth to encourage more energy into fruiting. Do this by digging a wider hole and putting sediment on the bottom. Then barricade the sides with bricks or metal sheets.

Garlic

HEALTH POWER ➕ Garlic, an antioxidant, slows plaque buildup (calcification) in coronary arteries. Studies show it stops calcium from binding with proteohepa-ran, (and then with LDL cholesterol) which begins the process. Slowing plaque buildup lowers the risk of later heart attack. Helps lower blood pressure and suppresses or removes oxidizing agents in blood stream and fat areas. Contains organosulphur compounds (ex. allicin and diallyl di-sulphide) that have antiviral and strong antibacterial activity, making garlic excellent for treating common colds. Compounds also help relax and enlarge blood vessels, which can help lower blood pressure and improve blood flow. These phytonutrients in garlic also show strong anti-carcino-gen effects. Contains anti-inflammatory compounds that reduce painful swelling from conditions like arthritis. Vitamins, minerals and phytonu-trients in garlic promote optimum general health.

VITAMIN & MINERAL ⬆ Vitamins – B6 (Pyridoxine), C and B1 (Thiamin)
Minerals – Manganese, Selenium, Calcium, Phosphorus and Copper

DISEASE PREVENTION 🚫 Reduces symptoms or risk of asthma, rheumatoid and osteoarthritis, di-abetes, heart disease and atherosclerosis. Reduces risk of, and impedes growth of, many cancers: oral, pharynx, esophageal, colorectal, laryngeal, breast, ovarian, prostate and kidney.

HOW TO GROW One of the easier bulb vegetables to grow and a great addition to many dishes. Grow best in areas with ample sun. Prefers deep soils with lots of organic matter. Mix in generous amounts of aged manure, compost or other planting mix containing high concentration of organic matter. The pH needs to be at or above 6.5; add lime to raise, if needed. Garlic grows from individual cloves that make up the bulb. To plant, dig 1.5-2 inch holes spaced 4-6 inches apart. Place one big clove with point facing up in each hole. Lightly mulch around plants to provide frost protection and water retention. In the far North, do it near winter's end or the start of spring. Elsewhere, fall is a good time to plant. For nice growth, keep rows and area weed free. In windy location, prop up longer stems with something to prevent snapping. Dig up bulbs in summer, dry with sun exposure and store in a net or basket.

INSECT CONTROL ✕ Rather pest free. Avoid diseases by preventing bulbs from sitting in standing water. Occasional viruses, but the worst they do is cut down yield a bit.

TIPS ✓ Weeds are biggest enemy; keep cleared. During spring, when leaves are emerging, encourage growth using an organic foliar spray. During the bulb-forming stage in early summer, prevent soil drying out.

Ginger

HEALTH POWER ✚ Ginger has been used for years to soothe gastrointestinal discomfort, including motion sickness, cold sweats, dizziness and vomiting. Effects are also seen in pregnant women. Antioxidant compounds (gingerols) suppress free radicals and reduce inflammation, thereby relieving pain. They may help protect the lipids in cell membranes from becoming damaged, preventing the loss of the important, internally produced antioxidant glutathione. High antioxidant activity supports cardiovascular health. Compounds in ginger help perspiration, a good way to detoxify during colds and other illness. Sweat has antimicrobial properties, helping protect against skin-borne infections.

VITAMIN & MINERAL ⬆ Vitamins – B6 (Pyridoxine)
Minerals – Potassium, Magnesium, Copper and Manganese

DISEASE PREVENTION ⊘ Consuming ginger regularly reduces inflammation and pain of rheumatoid and osteoarthritis. Gingerols may also help prevent different cancers from forming. In animal studies, gingerols have inhibited the growth of rectal and ovarian cancer cell lines or induced apoptosis (cell suicide).

HOW TO GROW ꙮ Ginger only sprouts when at temperatures of 75-80°F. These plants like sun, but will grow indoors if exposed to some sun. Great for container growing and does fine outdoors in a warm climate. Buy a plump ginger root with many buds from a trusted quality market. Soak overnight in warm water. For container growing, use those at least 1 foot deep full of highly fertile soil. Plant ginger roots just under the surface (2 inches deep) evenly spaced, with buds facing upward. Keep plant indoors in warmest, sunniest spot until it emerges above soil. Afterward, seasonally move container indoors and outdoors to keep plant in 75°F air. Keep sheltered from higher winds. Keep soil moist, but let it dry a bit between waterings. In warmer climates, plant roots any time. Amend soil with plenty of well-aged compost or planting mix. Ginger needs nutrient-rich soil with great drainage. Choose warm, sunny, sheltered spot. Soak fresh ginger roots the same way and plant out in spring when temperatures exceed 75°F. Ginger roots take a year or less to reach 2.5-4 feet tall. Harvest newer, younger sprouts in front of originals. Some can be used, frozen and/or replanted.

INSECT CONTROL ✕ Relatively insect and disease free. Some varieties bothered by spider mites or aphids. Usually you can shower and handpick to remove. If infestation is heavy, rinse off plant and use insecticidal soap. Planting French marigolds attracts aphid predators. Recommended, especially if growing other green-leafed vegetables nearby.

TIPS ✓ If the temperatures drop more than usual, cover them with either a row cover or plastic sheet to hold in some heat. The young stems are good for harvest at any point as they will hold a nice soft texture. Make sure the plant is indoors during cool weather (below 40 °F.) as it does not do well, and you will probably lose it if left outside then.

Globe Artichokes

HEALTH POWER + Almost no food or drink has more antioxidants than artichoke. (Came in #4 out of 1,000-plus in 2006 study.) Beat out blueberries, red wine, dark chocolate and tea. With a nice balance of nutrients, they are ideal for general health. High potassium prevents kidney stones. Folic acid supports cardiovascular health and helps prevent folate-deficiency birth defects. Contains cynarin, which triggers production of bile and aids digestion.

Contains phytonutrients that help stimulate regeneration of liver cells and improve gall bladder function, both improving detoxification and digestion. Great source of fiber, which promotes smooth digestion and helps regulate blood sugar and cholesterol. Low glycemic index and a good source of protein with no fat. High vitamin C defends body tissues from oxidative damage of free radicals.

VITAMIN & MINERAL

Vitamins – C, K and B9 (Folate)
Minerals – Magnesium, Potassium and Manganese

DISEASE PREVENTION

Contains many poly-phenol-type anti-oxidants shown to reduce risks of heart disease, cancer and birth defects. Help stimulate regeneration of liver cells, reduce blood cholesterol levels and improve digestion.

HOW TO GROW

A great addition to the garden and the dinner plate. Sensitive perennials needing moderate temperatures in winter. If winters freeze, you can treat them as annuals. Start with seeds indoors in winter or pick transplants in early spring from a quality local nursery. Avoid planting before final spring frost. Choose sunny, sheltered area of soil. Thoroughly mix in plenty of organic materials and/or fertilizer. If working with dense, heavier soils, try more organic matter to get good drainage. Plant roughly 18 inches apart. They grow up and sideways, spreading up to 5 feet by 5 feet in size. Deep beds give artichoke plants room for root growth, good drainage and high yields. Need a lot of water. Mulch the area with mature compost or manure, making sure to water on dry, hot days. In a colder climate, cut back plant in late fall and cover with a bushel basket or similar.

INSECT CONTROL

Damaged by a variety of slugs, which are most active feeding at night on soft plant tissues. Several ways to remove. In the evening, physically pick them off plant or soil and drop in a jar. Or cut bottom off a plastic jug and place over seedlings. As plants grow larger, use a larger plastic bottle and cut off the top, too. A dishful of beer sunk in the soil attracts them. They fall in and drown. For problem aphids, plant marigolds nearby to attract predator bugs (ladybugs and hoverflies). You can also rub off or spray off. If severe, use an organic insecticidal soap.

TIPS ✓ They like the soil just below neutral pH of 7. If pH is plus 7, add lime to bring down. When harvesting, expect 2-4 heads per plant. Cut off larger ones first, just before they open, to encourage smaller ones to grow to full size.

Grapefruit

HEALTH POWER ✚ Excellent source of Vitamin C, giving more than 100 percent of RDA. Protects immune system cells that fight the common colds/ other illness. Antioxidant reducing free radicals associated with inflammation, high cholesterol and cardiovascular disease. Pink grapefruit among the highest in antioxidants. Studies of antioxidant lycopene suggest regular eating can dramatically lower risk of prostate cancer. Many other phytonutrients with great potential benefits. Compounds called limonoids trigger production of detoxifying liver enzymes. Bonus: Limonoids stay active in body up to 24 hours, making them more potent fighter of many toxins, many of which could be carcinogenic. Red and blond grapefruit contain soluble fiber, pectin, that reduces bad form of cholesterol (LDL) and triglycerides, providing cardiovascular benefits by preventing buildup in arteries. Regular eating of high-C foods (juices of grapefruit, apple and orange) lowers risk of forming calcium oxalate (kidney) stones.

VITAMIN & MINERAL ⬆ Vitamins – C, A and B5 (Pantothenic Acid)
Minerals – Potassium

DISEASE PREVENTION ⊘ Helps reduce severity of inflammatory conditions like asthma, osteoarthritis and rheumatoid arthritis. Grapefruit linked to lower risk of cancers of prostate, breast, mouth, skin, stomach, colon and lung. Flavonoid naringenin linked with anti-cancer properties, especially of the prostate, via its ability to repair DNA. (As we age, lifelong cell divisions increase the frequency of "duplication errors" [mutations] in DNA.) Naringenin may promote the health of DNA by preventing mutations. Note: Although studied individually, many phytonutrients or antioxidants give their benefits not from their solo action but the synergy of many acting in concert. Thus, prefer to get your nutrition from natural sources (fruits and vegetables) rather than from chemicals synthesized into single-variety supplements in pill form.

HOW TO GROW

Grapefruit flesh similar to orange but larger and with sharper flavor. Some cultivars are yellow fleshed with seeds and slightly more tart in taste. Others have pink flesh, no seeds and generally sweeter. All varieties are self-fertilizing. Except that grapefruits need a few more nutrients, they are grown with the same soil requirements, maintenance, harvesting and pruning as oranges. See Oranges for details.

INSECT CONTROL

See Oranges, since these citrus cousins face the same pests.

TIPS

When planting, dig the bed deep when amending the soil with organic nutrients. For optimal health benefits, try eating a serving of grapefruit or similar fruit every day either as juice, part of a dish or raw.

Grapes

HEALTH POWER

Recent extensive research suggests most beneficial attributes may lie in their phytonutrients rather than vitamins and minerals. Most notable phytonutrients may be polyphenols, which include flavonoids and phenolic acids. Flavonoids quercetin and resveratrol help prevent free radicals from oxidizing the bad type of cholesterol (LDL), turning it into a form that later leads to arterial damage and plaque buildup. They maintain normal blood vessel dilation and prevent blood clots that can cause strokes. Contain saponins, believed to reduce absorption of cholesterol and slow the biochemical pathways leading to inflammation. Resveratrol and others play a large role in both of those health benefits and also prevent the secretion of the hormone angiotensin II, which can lead to stiffening of the heart. Contain pterostilbene, a promising compound for metabolizing fats, including cholesterol. Resveratrol, highly concentrated in red wine, is antibacterial and antifungal, making grapes a good fighter of food borne illness. Antioxidant action ditches free radicals and optimizes health of circulatory system, making grapes a great promoter of overall health. Nutrients available several ways: eating grapes fresh, drinking wine and juice or eating toast with grape jam.

VITAMIN & MINERAL

Vitamins – C, B1 (Thiamin) and B6 (Pyridoxine)
Minerals – Manganese and Potassium

Significantly reduces risk of heart disease and atherosclerosis. Research suggests consuming resveratrol may help protect DNA from damage leading to lung cancer or other damage leading to prostate, liver, colorectal and breast cancer. May also lower risk of Alzheimer's disease.

DISEASE PREVENTION

HOW TO GROW

Grapes prefer sunny site with great drainage. Produce fruit from second year forward. Self-fertile, so not essential to grow more than one variety. (Nice to have a few different flavors.) Many different cultivars make it possible to grow grapes almost everywhere. Certain locations (like the Deep South) suitable to grow grapes only for jelly, juice or wine. Ask experts what varieties and types work best in your area. Before planting, amend the soil around the planting area with plenty of organic matter and adjust the pH to around 6.0. Get year-old vines from nursery. Support with a wire or grow along a fence or over an arch in backyard. Nurseryman can tell you how to train them. Soak roots in a bucket of water with a handful of micronutrient rich fertilizer for a few hours before planting. Plant 5 feet apart in spring while still dormant before buds begin to swell. Once planted, cut each vine down to leave just two or three healthy looking buds. After planting and each spring, mulch underneath the area with well-aged compost or manure. If growing grapes to eat fresh, prune out any odd-shaped or diseased, and remove berries regularly in random spots in each cluster to allow others to grow larger. Harvest when stems turn brown and fruit is nice and sweet. Cut off clusters with pruning shears and store in cool, shady spot where they will last for about a month.

INSECT CONTROL

Pests include birds, wasps, grape berry moths, Japanese beetles and red spider mite. Birds can be completely stopped only by covering with netting or some type of row cover. Birds also love mulberries. Plant a mulberry tree nearby to help distract them away from grapes. To control wasps, fill a container with a sweet liquid (like juice) and cover the container with a lid having a small hole. Wasps will crawl in and not find their way out. Grape berry moths lay eggs on the flowers; purplish larvae feed on buds and flowers. Hang pheromone traps to control. For Japanese beetles, shake them off in the morning and set out bait containers that trap them. Most nurseries have pheromone or other baited traps. To stop red spider mite, keep plants moist by regular spraying with water. If resilient, spray with organic insecticidal soap or oil.

TIPS ✓ If the growth seems slow, apply a handful per vine of nutrient-rich fertilizer like kelp meal, fish bone meal, or alfalfa meal. One study found red wine contains about triple the valuable phytonutrients (like resveratrol) of white wine. Downside of regular wine drinking is the adverse affects of alcohol. Avoid this by drinking alcohol-free wine or 3 glasses of grape juice daily.

Guava

HEALTH POWER ✚ Loaded with vitamin C (more than double the RDA per fruit) and beneficial phytonutrients. Vitamin C is a powerful antioxidant that prevents damage to many cells, organs and tissues such as eyes, blood vessels, heart and immune system. Full dose of vitamin C in one fruit assures water-soluble areas get protection from free radicals and that immune cells are active. High in lycopene, a powerful antioxidant known to reduce oxidative damage in cells. May also inhibit growth of some types of cancer cells. (Undergoing extensive research.) Fiber and potassium enable guava to lower blood pressure, blood glucose, plaque buildup in blood vessels, cholesterol and triglycerides while promoting smooth digestion. Some phytonutrients in guava have antibacterial and anti-fungal action that may help fight off common microbes (such as Staphylococcus, Shigella, Salmonella, Bacillus, E. coli, Clostridium, and Pseudomonas genera).

VITAMIN & MINERAL ⬆ Vitamins – C, A, B9 (Folate) and traces of others
Minerals – Potassium, Copper, Manganese and traces of others

DISEASE PREVENTION 🚫 Guava may help protect against asthma, rheumatoid and osteoarthritis, atherosclerosis, heart disease and cancers of prostate, lung, stomach, colon and many others. Can help reduce symptoms of gastroenteritis, recurring diarrhea and other digestive problems.

HOW TO GROW 🐛 Guava is a small, tropical native tree producing delectable green fruit with tender light-yellow or red/pink interior. Grow best in temperature range of 45-90°F. To produce fruit, mean temperature must remain above 60°F. for up to six months (depending on the cultivar). Mature trees can withstand an occasional light frost, but young trees die right away. Choose site with full sun where wind does not exceed 10-15 mph for long periods. Guavas tolerate soil types (except compacted) and pH range 5-8. For best fruit production, roots must penetrate well into soil. For full nutrient supply and good drainage, work in some fertile plant mix rich in organic matter several weeks before planting. If you have not planned ahead, hold off adding mix or fertilizer. If soil consistency is bad, mix in regular soil 1 to 1. Buy a resistant, healthy transplant from a reputable local nursery. If planting more than one tree, space minimum 7-10 feet apart. Dig a hole 3-4 times the diameter of the root ball and 3 times deeper. Position tree in the hole so that root ball lies just beneath soil surface. Fill hole and pat down to remove air pockets. Stake tree the first year so roots get nicely anchored. Use soft fabric to tie stake to tree so as not to damage trunk. Mulch over root zone, keeping 1 foot away from trunk. In first year, fertilize about 5 times (every couple months) with highly fertile, well-balanced mix with full range of macro and micronutrients. As tree grows larger, apply more fertilizer each time. Prune young tree during first year at around 1-2 feet high to promote branching. Also tip branches at 2-3 feet to promote more branching. Harvest just as fruit softens to the touch and is easily removed. Store harvested fruit in a cool place away from sun.

INSECT CONTROL ✗ Guava trees can be infested by a number of insects, diseases and nematodes. For most effective treatment, consult local county agricultural extension service or nearby nursery.

TIPS ✓ For best flavor, let guavas ripen on the tree. Even in cooler temperatures, they do not store long when fully ripe. Or pick them when still a bit firm just before ripening. You can then store them up to five weeks in cool temperatures. To speed up the ripening process, put them in a paper bag with a banana or apple.

Horseradish

HEALTH POWER + Horseradish contains glucosinolates (ex. isothiocyanate), potent phytonutrients promoting synthesis of compounds that fight cancer and suppress synthesis of compounds fueling cancer cell growth. Research suggests effects come not from isothiocyanate alone, but from synergistic action with other vegetables containing isothiocyanate. Also linked with increasing blood flow in infected areas and increasing liver's ability to detoxify. Many people use its antimicrobial properties as remedy for cold, flu and fever. Here's how: Blend or grind up tablespoon of fresh horseradish and add to boiling water. Steep for about 5 minutes. Drink this brew 2-3 times per day for fever relief. Can be an effective nasal decongestant by adding to food or eating straight. (Watch out for strong taste.) Excellent source of vitamin C and a little fiber. Small amounts of other vitamins and minerals.

VITAMIN & MINERAL

Vitamins – C and B9 (Folate)
Minerals – Potassium, Manganese and Magnesium

DISEASE PREVENTION

Horseradish may reduce the risk or onset of prostate cancer (and potentially many others from isothiocyanate action) and infections leading to coughs, colds, flu and urinary tract infections.

HOW TO GROW

Be careful. While this perennial root crop can be grown for a fantastic fish and meat sauce, it can proliferate beyond control. A crucifer like broccoli and cabbages, it prefers rich, water retentive soil. Digging deeply to loosen soil allows roots to grow thick and straight down several feet. In early spring, plant root pieces with the thinner end down and the thicker end 3-4 inches below surface. Space plants 1 foot apart and rows 4 feet apart. Horseradish spreads rapidly by its roots and fills void in no time. To harness its growth, dig up all roots each year and replant only a select few. Or let it grow in an area where space is plentiful and nothing is adjacent. Or grow in container or embed a pot/bucket in soil to block roots from spreading out. Not invasive. When horseradish gets established, it usually stays the same size. Once planted, water to keep soil moist. Hot summer days require more watering, but make sure to water well in late summer and early fall when they grow the most. Harvest a few young spring leaves to add to salads. Roots are ready to harvest in fall (October-November). Quite hardy. If not harvested, will sprout again in spring.

INSECT CONTROL

Very resilient. No pest problems that threaten production or plant life.

TIPS

Can be companion planted next to potatoes to repel Colorado potato beetles.

Kale

+

Kale is highly nutritious, with large variety of vitamins, minerals and phytonutrients. An ideal, all-in-one vegetable to add to your regular diet. Phytonutrients containing sulfur help activate detoxifying enzymes, which act synergistically to remove potentially toxic/carcinogenic chemicals. Other phyotchemicals in crucifers, like glucosinolates, metabolize to isothiocyanates, which inhibit development of many cancer cells. Great for vision. Carotenoids, like lutein and zeaxanthin, along with beta-carotene and vitamins A and C, protect from damaging free radicals and ultraviolet light. Antioxidant action of vitamins A and C help boost immune system, protect blood vessels, reduce inflammation and protect epithelial cells (skin and lining of internal organs). Vitamin K with calcium enhances bone-forming processes and helps prevent bone loss. Trace mineral manganese, along with the B vitamins, helps metabolize sugars, carbohydrates, proteins and lipids to produce energy. Eating leafy vegetables has been shown to extend cognitive function for years longer among elders. Excellent source of fiber, which promotes healthy digestion and regulates cholesterol and blood sugar levels.

VITAMIN & MINERAL ⬆

Vitamins – K, A, C, B6 (Pyridoxine), E, B2 (Riboflavin), B1 (Thiamin), B9 (Folate) and B3 (Niacin)
Minerals – Manganese, Copper, Calcium, Potassium, Iron, Magnesium and Phosphorus

DISEASE PREVENTION 🚫

May play significant role in reducing symptoms or onset of cancers in ovaries, breast, colon, prostate, lung and bladder, plus cataracts, rheumatoid and osteoarthritis and cardiovascular disease.

HOW TO GROW 🌱

A nutritious, hardy leaf vegetable that can grow in tough winters. Ask local nursery which varieties are best for your area. Choose semi-shady, moderately sheltered site. Soil pH should be near 6.8. Add lime, if needed. Amend soil by mixing in plenty of well-aged compost, manure or a planting mix rich in organic matter. Kale likes cooler weather but still grows in warmer climates during cooler months. In cooler areas, sow seeds outdoors in late spring for fall and winter harvesting. In warmer areas, sow seeds outdoors through early fall for late winter and spring harvests. Create shallow drills as long as desired, spacing each drill out by about 2.5

feet. Plant seeds half inch deep and 2 feet apart within rows. Cover with a thin layer of soil and water regularly. During growth, handpick or hoe out weeds out as they appear. Mulching helps deter weeds and holds in moisture. Harvest young and softer leaves from the center of the plant as needed, not all at once. Larger, tougher leaves are great for cooking.

INSECT CONTROL ✗ Kale generally less susceptible to pests than other crucifers. See Broccoli, Brussels Sprouts and Cauliflower for general pest control. Others include cabbage root maggot, cabbage butterfly and club root. Cabbage root maggots can be stopped by applying small plastic or foam ground covers that tightly wrap around the base of seedlings. Butterfly can be stopped by hand picking caterpillar and rubbing eggs off leaves. Club root is an incurable soil disease that can last 10 years. The only way around it is to transplant well-developed, resistant seedlings. This allows plants to have acceptable yield but stops club root infection.

TIPS ✓ For continuous harvest, make successive sowings through start of growing seasons.

Kiwi

HEALTH POWER + Kiwi fruit contain a solid mix of vitamins, minerals, and phytonutrients for a daily health boost. Research is still ongoing, but certain phytonutrients (probably carotenoids and flavonoids) in kiwi can decrease oxygen-related damage to DNA. Damage to DNA molecules can cause mutations that interfere with proteins and enzymes vital to all cellular functions. Studies show eating kiwis or other citrus fruits lowers the risk of respiratory problems. Highly concentrated source of natural vitamin C, the primary water-soluble antioxidant that neutralizes free radicals causing cellular damage, most notably in cardiovascular system, respiratory system, joints and immune cells. Fat-soluble antioxidant vitamin E gives some protection to fatty areas of the body. Good source of fiber, which reduces high blood sugar and cholesterol levels and helps remove toxins from the colon. The minerals in kiwi (magnesium, potassium and copper) support cardiovascular health. Some work individually, others synergistically, to reduce blood clotting, plaque buildup, triglyceride levels and blood pressure.

VITAMIN & MINERAL

Vitamins – C and E
Minerals – Potassium, Copper, Magnesium and Manganese

DISEASE PREVENTION

Kiwi may reduce symptoms related to or the onset of rheumatoid and osteoarthritis, asthma, macular degeneration, colon cancer (and potentially many others), atherosclerosis, cardiovascular disease and diabetic heart disease.

HOW TO GROW

Kiwis are a nice ornamental for the garden. Yields tasty treats with more than triple the vitamin C in oranges. Two main varieties, one hardy to as low as -40°F.; the other down to 10°F. Hardier variety has smooth skin and is the size of large grapes. Less hardy Chinese Kiwi are larger, fuzzy type we see more often at markets. Except for pruning, they need little maintenance and give high yield if trellised. If growing in colder region, main trunk of Chinese Kiwi needs winter protection. Except for a couple cultivars, most kiwis are not self-fertile. For non-self-fertilizing, plant 3-4 females per male. Most kiwis like full sun, but some prefer partial shade in warmer climates. They like well-drained soil at pH 6-6.5. To spread, kiwis need some help. Grow them along a sturdy trellis or strong fence. Work some compost or planting mix into soil to enrich with nutrients and organic matter and to create a nice loam. In spring, plant vines and trim back to 4 or 5 buds. When they grow a bit, choose one as main shoot/trunk. Secure it to trellis or fence so it grows upward. When it reaches the top, cut the tip to encourage growth of lateral branches. Every month in summer, prune new growth back to 4-5 buds for denser growth with large fruit clusters. Water enough to keep soil moist, taking care not to over water. At the beginning of each growing season, reapply a large amount of fertilizer rich in organic matter (aged compost, manure or planting mix). Kiwis need lots of nutrients. Vines give fruit 2-3 years after planting. For longer-lasting kiwis, pick off the vine in late summer right before they ripen. Let them ripen indoors. You can preserve some even longer in the refrigerator.

INSECT CONTROL

Few pests or diseases plague the kiwi plant. If infestation is large, get advice from your local nursery or agricultural extension office.

TIPS

Remove soft, aged or damaged kiwis from fresh storage to prevent disease transmission or mass softening of fruit. Even the smallest damage can cause the release of ethylene, making other fruit ripen too quickly.

Lavender

HEALTH POWER +

The soothing aroma in lavender plants alone is enough to calm the nerves after a tough day. Many say having the fragrance sprayed (or placed using the plant itself) on their pillow or in the bed linen gives headache relief and better sleep. Scientific studies support this phenomenon. Making it into a tea or extracting the oil can provide similar medicinal properties, such as reducing stress, anxiety, nervousness and nausea. Lavender's fragrance and soothing effects can be a great addition to body, bath and cleaning products. Lavender's essential oil has antibacterial and antifungal action. Lavender oil is great to have for applying to dressing of wounds and burns. Can be used for cooking to add a bit of flavor. Some create lavender sugar by leaving in a sugar container for a couple weeks. You can also grind it up and use it to bake or give flavor to anything you think needs it.

VITAMIN & MINERAL ⬆

Non-sufficient data

DISEASE PREVENTION 🚫

Lavender is great for preventing microbial infections in wounds or burns. Its fragrance and oil extracts may also help treat insomnia, motion sickness and depression.

HOW TO GROW 🌱

Lavender is an attractive fragrant perennial herb with purple flowers. About 30 species of this plant are known. The most popular for oil extraction is true (or English) lavender. They prefer site with full sun, superb soil drainage and excellent air circulation. The pH should be between 6.5-7.5. Amend soil with some all-purpose organic planting mix. Plant seedlings in spring when temperatures stay above freezing and soil is warming. Space them out about 20 inches. Water regularly in the beginning, but lightly. (Over watering quickly leads to root rot.) When fully mature, lavender plants are drought tolerant and need little water. Mulch annually to provide a little nutritional boost or insulate during winter. If attempting to grow in non-optimal conditions, plant in pots with holes in the bottom so you have option to take indoors during threatening weather. Lavender needs a couple of years before ready to harvest, even more if the goal is to extract oil (4-5 years). Harvest in morning hours when scent is the strongest.

| INSECT CONTROL | ✗ | No common pest issues exist for lavenders. |

| TIPS | ✓ | Using a bath bag filled with lavender, steep it in water for a soothing, muscle relaxing soak. |

Leeks

| HEALTH POWER | + | Leeks are in the Allium family and carry some of the same health benefits as garlic and onions. (See Garlic and Onion entries for the benefits of phytonutrients in this family.) Leeks differ from their family members in giving fewer nutrients per weight. Because they are less concentrated, you must eat more to get the same nutrition. Compared to garlic and onion, this is easy considering how mellow and sweet their taste is. In general, regular eating of veggies in the Allium family is linked with lower bad cholesterol concentrations and preventing or inhibiting the growth or spread of cancer. With a small dose of vitamin C, iron, folate and B6, leeks add a few antioxidants to get rid of dangerous free radicals, help activate hemoglobin molecules for oxygen transport, lower high levels of the compound homocysteine (damages blood vessels at high concentrations), and helps the body metabolize food to provide energy. |

| VITAMIN & MINERAL | ↑ | Vitamins – C, B9 (Folate) and B6 (Pyridoxine)
Minerals – Manganese and Iron |

| DISEASE PREVENTION | ⊘ | With regular eating, leeks team up with other Allium veggies to help reduce the symptoms or prevent development of atherosclerosis, heart disease, prostate and colon cancer, ovarian cancer and many other cancers. |

| HOW TO GROW | ✿ | Leeks are great to grow for a winter harvest. They need little attention and are hardy through all but the coldest winters when the soil gets too hard to dig. Choose a site with plenty of sunshine. Work in a generous dose of organic matter in the form of aged compost, manure or planting mix. They prefer a soil pH around 6.5. Add lime to raise, if needed. The pale color we are used to seeing near the bottom of leeks comes from the blanching process during cultivation. There are two ways to do this. First, |

you can multiple sow them in seed trays in mid-spring. Fill each cell with highly fertile soil (peat and planting mix). Make a small dip in each cell and place 6-7 seeds in each. Cover the seeds with a fine medium such as sand, cover with plastic, water well, and place on a windowsill, under a florescent light or in the greenhouse at or near 60°F. Once germinated, remove the plastic. When they reach 1-2 inches, they are ready to plant out (around early summer). Plant them about 10 inches apart in rows spaced 10 inches apart. Stagger the rows this way to prevent overcrowding. For an alternative technique that blanches each plant, sow seeds 6 inches apart outdoors in a shallow drill in mid-to-late spring. When they reach a couple inches tall, transplant them into pre-made dibber holes 6-8 inches deep. Place one plant per hole and space the holes out by 6 inches. Space rows out by 1 foot. Don't fill the hole with soil. Instead, water each hole a little after placing the leek to get some soil over the roots. As they grow, keep the area weed free by hoeing. Also, to keep the blanch going, push some soil up around the base throughout the growing season. Leeks are ready to harvest in mid-fall. They can be left in the ground until needed unless the weather will make the soil too hard to dig them up. In that case, dig them up early and store in a moist peat soil.

| **INSECT CONTROL** | ✕ | Leeks are usually pest free. If you have problems, consult your local nursery. |

| **TIPS** | ✓ | Companion plant leeks next to carrots and celery since they repel carrot fly. Do not plant next to beans, peas or parsley. |

Lemon Grass

| **HEALTH POWER** | + | Including lemon grass in your garden provides many benefits. Making tea with the stems helps digestion, promotes a calm night's sleep, reduces anxiety, eases headaches and even has antimicrobial abilities to fight some infections. It may help with respiratory problems and provide some calming effects as well. Adding lemongrass to the bath will help clear up oily skin. Lemon grass citronella oil is a natural, effective mosquito repellent. To get the oil directly from the plant, break off a stalk and peel off the outer leaves until you find a scallion-like stem at the base. Bend and rub with your palms until it turns juicy. Then rub thoroughly over exposed |

skin. Planting these plants around the patio will help deter mosquitoes. Lemon grass is able to repel fleas and ticks in the same way. If you are walking your dog through deep grasses, lemon grass can be a quick help for both of you. As a detoxifying agent, lemon grass has a diuretic effect (causing more urination) which helps flush out the kidney, liver, pancreas, bladder and digestive tract. Loaded with beneficial minerals, which can lower blood pressure, maintain healthy nerve/muscle function and act as co-factors for enzymes with many diverse functions.

VITAMIN & MINERAL

Vitamins – B9 (Folate) and B2 (Riboflavin)
Minerals – Manganese, Iron, Potassium, Magnesium, Zinc, Copper and Phosphorus

DISEASE PREVENTION

Lemon grass in your diet can only help, but we need more research before we can say it helps prevent disease. Very high manganese gives enzymes all over the body their co-factor and maintains the biochemical balance necessary for health. Good source of iron to help prevent anemia. Lowering blood pressure takes some stress off the cardiovascular system and may help prevent heart problems.

HOW TO GROW

Popular in Asian cuisine, lemon grass grows easily and has many uses from adding to fresh dishes to drying out to brew tea. Grows best in tropical regions, but also grows outdoors in warmer, temperate regions with a healthy dose of compost/planting mix and full sun. Alternatively, you can grow in slightly cooler climates in pots. Bring them indoors during the cool months and keep them in a sunny location. To grow lemon grass, pick up the greenest, healthiest looking plant with bulbs and roots still attached, if possible. Trim off the top couple of inches, get rid of any dead-looking growth and set the stalks down into a container of room temperature water in a sunny location (window sill). After the roots have matured a bit, take the started plant out of the water and set it down in fertile soil with the crown just below the surface. If you live in a climate where it gets cooler in the winters, plant in pots and place in a sunny, warm location of the patio or house. Lemon grass cannot survive freezing temperatures, so be swift to bring them indoors when temperatures drop. In warmer areas, plant outdoors in full sun. Water regularly to keep the soil damp, not soggy. Outdoor plants can reach 4-6 feet high and 6-8 feet wide, so allow them room to spread.

INSECT CONTROL ✗ Few problems with pests; none that threaten the life of the plant. In companion planting, some gardeners repel melon flies by planting and trimming lemon grass near their crop.

TIPS ✓ Buy more than one stalk at the market to use as a backup if one or more plants do not sprout roots during initiation.

Lemons & Limes

HEALTH POWER + A great source of vitamin C and other phytonutrients, similar to other popular fruits and veggies. Vitamin C is the great immune booster and antioxidant that knocks out free radicals at the top of the inflammatory cascade. Helps reduce symptoms of inflammatory conditions like rheumatoid arthritis. Acting against free radicals, vitamin C can assist in cardiovascular health by preventing the oxidation of cholesterol, a step toward plaque buildup. Lemons and limes both have flavonoid compounds that act as antioxidants, too. Both help sterilize some foods by killing off bacteria. Citrus fruits also contain limonoids that fight a number of cancers and potentially lower cholesterol.

VITAMIN & MINERAL ↑ Vitamins – C
Minerals – Many but none of significant daily value

DISEASE PREVENTION ⊘ Immune system health and cell protection (possibly against cancer) come from antioxidant concentration of lemons and limes. The citrus limonoids defend against cancers of the mouth, skin, lung, breast, stomach and colon. The flavonoids may prove to protect against many common disease-causing bacteria.

HOW TO GROW Naturally subtropical, all citrus fruits need protection from frost. An exception, the Meyer lemon can handle brief temperatures below freezing in a protected spot. Pick a protected site with plenty of sun. Prefer soil on the heavy side. Amend the site generously with aged compost, manure or highly fertile planting mix. Soil pH should be 6-6.5. Raise beds 1.5 feet above ground. Plant trees any time of the year, especially in the South, but spring and fall are usually best times. Plant tree so that grafting point is a few inches above soil level. Space multiple trees 15-20 feet apart to avoid competition for nutrients or sunlight. Best way to feed is by applying organic fruit tree fertilizers, kelp meal, fish bone meal, alfalfa meal, organic composts or compost tea. Keep tree well watered, especially in first few years. If tree becomes thick and bushy, remove a branch for better airflow and light absorption. Prune shoots that point inward or have dead/diseased spots. Cut fruit off tree when ripe and use or store. To store, place fruit in a container and surround with dry sand or dirt to preserve for several months. Tree produces fruit all year in moderate climates.

INSECT CONTROL ✗ See Oranges, which have identical pests as lemons/limes.

TIPS ✓ Once all fruit is removed from a shoot, trim it back to 5 inches to encourage more fruit-bearing shoots.

Lettuce

HEALTH POWER + Loaded with good stuff: Vitamins K, A, C, folate and manganese. Romaine especially supports cardiovascular health. Vitamins A and C help prevent arterial plaque buildup by eliminating free radicals that oxidize cholesterol and help keep arterial walls elastic. Fiber helps regulate cholesterol levels and promotes healthy digestion. Romaine lettuce's potassium may help reduce blood pressure and promote the proper firing of muscle and nerve cells. Folate helps prevent damage to blood vessel walls by lowering homocysteine concentration in blood. Folate also is essential for proper nerve development in fetuses. A few ounces of romaine lettuce give more than 100 percent RDA of vitamin K, which helps in making thicker bones. To help avoid lethargy, B vitamins and manganese in romaine help the body extract energy from food.

VITAMIN & MINERAL ↑ Vitamins – K, A, C, B9 (Folate), B1 (Thiamin), B2 (Riboflavin), B3 (Niacin), and B6 (Pyridoxine)
Minerals – Manganese, Chromium, Potassium, Molybdenum, Iron, Phosphorus and Calcium

DISEASE PREVENTION ⊘ Romaine lettuce may reduce the risk or symptoms of cardiovascular disease, rheumatoid and osteoarthritis and macular degeneration. Provides general defense from many common cancers via synergistic effect of vitamins, minerals and phytonutrients acting as antioxidants, detoxifiers and possibly direct inhibitors of cancer cell growth.

HOW TO GROW

Great veggie to have in the garden for summer harvest. May grow all year round in moderate climates. Many lettuce varieties. Some mature quickly or slowly, are tolerant to heat; others that grow back after you cut them. Lettuce prefers a cooler spot. Choose a site with part shade if your garden gets warm. Soil pH should be near 6.5. Amend soil modestly with well-aged compost or planting mix; too much fresh treatment leads to rotting. Sow seeds in trays indoors around 65°F. under fluorescent lights or in greenhouse in late winter. After seedlings develop, prepare for transplanting outdoors by cooling temperature down to 50°F. In early spring, transplant seedlings 6 inches apart in rows 6 inches apart, underneath cloches if temperature is too cold. At the same time, sow a larger, later variety outdoors underneath the cloche. Continue to sow a new row of seeds in open ground every couple of weeks for successive harvesting, with the last sowing in midsummer. Keep soil moist by watering as needed. When heads look full and feel firm, pull plants and cut their roots.

INSECT CONTROL

Cutworms, aphids, millipedes, and slugs are common lettuce pests. Cutworms live beneath soil and feed on the base of plants. If a plant falls due to its base being eaten, hoe around (without damaging roots) to expose worms to birds. Put cutworm collars on transplants if you have problems. Regulate aphids by planting French marigolds to attract hover flies and ladybugs, their natural predators. Millipedes are little black insects that live below the soil and feed on roots. They hide and breed under rocks or loose/fallen plant matter during daytime. Best way to control is keep garden area clean. Check under rocks and other hiding spots during the day. For slugs, embed a cup of beer in soil. They crawl into it and drown.

TIPS

If roots look infected, burn or dispose to prevent later return.

Licorice

HEALTH POWER

The phytonutrients in licorice have been used for centuries as a natural remedy for many common ailments. Prepare as a tea, make lozenges or simply chew on the root. Stores carry it as an extract, powder or loose leaves. Many use it to help aid digestive problems, like indigestion, heartburn and irregularity; has mild laxative properties. May help produce energy and increase stamina. Most popular use is to relieve chest congestion, coughs or sore throats. Glycoside stimulates production of thin mucus in membranes of stomach and respiratory tract and helps clear out lungs and throat. Useful as a soothing skin ointment. Has antimicrobial properties (including antiviral and antibacterial). Inhibits the hepatitis virus. Some women use licorice root as a dietary supplement to relieve premenstrual syndrome and symptoms of menopause. Research suggests this effect comes from preventing spikes in estrogen levels. May also help decrease mood swings and hot flashes. Not to be used during pregnancy, because it is linked to increased risk of premature labor. Side effects of prolonged use include water retention and lower potassium levels. Use caution and consult physician if you have high blood pressure or heart disease.

VITAMIN & MINERAL

Vitamins – A, B1 (Thiamin), B2 (Riboflavin), B5 (Niacin), B6 (Pyridoxine), Folate & E

Minerals – Calcium, Iron, Magnesium, Manganese, Phosphorus, Potassium and Sodium

DISEASE PREVENTION

May relieve symptoms of ulcers, eczema, psoriasis, hepatitis C, bronchitis, sore throat, bronchial asthma and acid reflux.

HOW TO GROW

Native to Southern Europe, licorice grows as a perennial legume developing into a thin shrub with pretty lilac pea flowers. Prefers full sun and tolerates different soil types. Takes 3-4 years for roots to mature for harvest. Simple to grow but requires initial preparation. Scratch the surface of each seed with sandpaper or a file and soak in water for 24 hours. Fill 4-inch pots with soil/planting mix. Pack down firmly. Place each mini pot in a tray that can hold an inch or more of water. Fill tray with water and let soil saturate. Poke ¼-inch holes 1 inch apart in the center of each pot and place licorice seeds down one per hole. Fill holes with ¼ inch of soil. Place tray with pots where they will get 8-10 hours of filtered light and temperature between 60-70°F. Keep seedlings soil moist but not sopping. Transplant outdoors in spring. Clear site of weeds and work planting mix/aged compost into soil to achieve high fertility, water retention and good drainage. Prefers pH close to 6. Dig holes same depth as 4-inch pots and a bit wider. Plant seedlings 2.5-3 feet apart. Remove seedling along with its soil by turning the pot upside down and sliding it out. Place down in their holes and fill the hole with well amended fertile soil. Water deeply during the first year, keeping soil moist. After first year, water only in dry weather. Roots ready to harvest 3-4 years after planting.

INSECT CONTROL ✗ No real pests threaten healthy maturation.

TIPS ✓ To extract the essential oils, chop and clean the roots. Soak the roots (if dried) overnight to plump them up. Place them in food processor or blender with equal amounts of water. Grind them down so root pieces are the size of sand particles. Pour water and root mixture into pot, cover (to retain volatile portions of oil), and simmer on low heat for an hour or more. Turn heat off, let cool, strain the roots out, place liquid in light-proof container, cover and refrigerate.

Loquat

HEALTH POWER + A great fruit low in saturated fat and sodium while high in a few vitamins, minerals and fiber. Good to eat while trying to lose weight. Vitamin A, a protective antioxidant, promotes eyesight, especially night vision. Also helps maintain healthy teeth, immune system, and skeletal and soft tissue (skin and membranes around organs). Fiber adds bulk to a meal, giving a full feeling faster that may help control weight. Promotes smooth digestion and lowers elevated cholesterol and blood sugar. B vitamins are necessary to encourage the breakdown (catabolism) and buildup (anabolism) of compounds in foods and vital nutrients needed for healthy function, respectively. Vitamin B6 helps immune system produce antibodies and break down proteins. Vitamin B12 helps form red blood cells and, with potassium, helps maintain healthy nerve function. Potassium also reduces elevated blood pressure and helps maintain proper functioning of muscle cells. Manganese is an important cofactor for enzymes involved with many functions like disarming free radicals, forming bone/cartilage, metabolism and wound healing.

VITAMIN & MINERAL

Vitamins – A, B6 (Pyridoxine) and B12 (Cobalamins)
Minerals – Manganese and Potassium

DISEASE PREVENTION

Loquats may help defend against infectious diseases while helping lower risk or symptoms of diabetes, heart disease, osteoporosis and cancers of the lung, skin, breast, liver, colon and prostate.

HOW TO GROW

Comes from an evergreen tree native to subtropics. Find a healthy transplant at a trusted local nursery. Choose a site with full sun and enough space away from buildings or other trees. Grows to average 20-30 feet. Spring is fruiting season. If spring frosts are a concern, plant in warmest part of garden. Tolerates many soil consistencies. Main requirement is good drainage. Dig a hole three times deeper than the root structure and triple the diameter of the tree. Work in plenty of aged compost or planting mix to the soil dug out. Fill the hole a bit and place the tree so that the top of the root crown matches ground level. Fill hole and pack down a bit. If your area has a low water table or is prone to flooding, plant tree higher in a raised mound. After planting, lay down a thick layer of mulch over the root zone, taking care to leave about a foot between base of trunk and mulch layer. Water thoroughly after planting. Water every other day for first 4 weeks, unless it's raining. After a few years of growth, water tree only during longer dry periods and during fruiting. Fertilize every few months the first year and every 4-6 months every subsequent year. During fruiting season, remove half the loquats when they are pea size to increase fruit size and quality. Throughout the first couple years, prune shoots after harvest by tipping them when they reach 2-3 feet long. Prune older trees to restrain their growth. When pruning, aim to increase sun exposure and airflow to all foliage while promoting strong, healthy fruiting. When effectively pruned, loquat trees can be maintained around 10 feet.

INSECT CONTROL

Main pests are birds and bees. If both are present at full force during fruiting season, preserve the fruit by bagging each cluster. Also try setting out hanging traps for bees and growing other trees, such as mulberry, to attract birds.

TIPS

Don't plant grass near the base of trunk. Lawn mowing and weed eating can damage and even kill the tree. If planting in a windy, exposed area, stake the tree the first few years.

Mango

HEALTH POWER

Mangoes are a great source of powerful antioxidants such as beta-carotene, vitamin C, quercetin and astragalin. They combine to neutralize free radicals, which can damage cells in the form of DNA mutations that lead to uncontrolled cell division, i.e. cancer. The antioxidants zeaxanthin and lutein help stop age-related macular degeneration in the eye. Vitamin C helps the immune system and assists in preventing cataracts. The soluble fiber, pectin, lowers cholesterol, promotes healthy digestion and cardio-vascular function. Pectin also helps reduce the risk of gastrointestinal cancer. The high iron content helps women recover after menstruation and assists during pregnancy. High potassium helps maintain healthy nerve signal transmission and muscle contraction. Contain proteolytic enzymes that help break down proteins and work with fiber for healthy digestion.

VITAMIN & MINERAL

Vitamins – A, C, B9 (Folate), B6 (Pyridoxine), B2 (Riboflavin), B1 (Thiamin), E & K
Minerals – Copper, Iron, Potassium, Phosphorus, Calcium, Magnesium and Selenium

DISEASE PREVENTION

The high iron content in mangoes can help prevent or reduce the symptoms of anemia. Vitamin C reduces inflammation and pain in rheumatoid arthritis, osteoarthritis and asthma. Antioxidants with vitamin E and selenium help ward off many cancers and heart disease.

HOW TO GROW

Easy to grow this delectable fruit from the tropics, but are very sensitive to cold. Below 40°F they go dormant and die below 32°F. In an area like Florida, where it only frosts a few times a year, deal with it by manually protecting with a plastic cover. To start growth, buy the healthiest mango you can find and eat it, being careful not to disturb the husk inside. Wash off the husk and let the seed dry out for several days. Gently split open the husk with a butter knife and remove the seed inside. If it is starting to grow a root, keep it attached. Fill a small pot (6-8 inches) with fertile soil and a little planting mix. Moisten the soil and make a small pocket in the center of the pot. Place the seed with the rounded side just above the surface and cover all but the very tip of the seed with soil. Don't water for a couple days. Place the seed in a sunny, warm location. Cover the pot with a slightly perforated plastic to increase humidity and temperature. A greenhouse is ideal. Keep soil moist and wait for the seed to sprout. In a warmer area, transplant the seedling with the ball of potting soil in a bed of well draining fertile soil in a warm, sunny, protected area. You can also transplant to a bigger pot if you need to keep it inside for warmth during cooler months. Fertilize a few times during the first year (except in winter) and keep soil moist but not soggy. While the tree is young, keep the area around the trunk weed free. It takes 3-7 years for the tree to bear fruit. Fruit is ripe and ready when it gives a little to a squeeze.

INSECT CONTROL ✗ White flies, aphids, spider mites, scales and thrips are the main mango pests. Hang a yellow card covered in sticky grease to attract and trap white flies. Plant French marigolds to attract aphid predators. Scales are disc shaped insects that hold themselves tightly to leaves, eat them and secrete honeydew that kills leaves. Watch for scales and scrape them off as soon as you see them. Thrips are too small to see, but their dark droppings are visible. Leaves appear wilted or bleached. Introduce predatory mites as a biological control. If infestation is large, spray with insecticidal soap.

TIPS ✓ When the main shoot reaches 3-4 feet long, trim it to encourage more side shoots to form. Prune any branches that over crowd the tree for optimal sunlight and air circulation. Sometimes you can find a transplant that is already a year old and closer to fruit bearing.

Marjoram

HEALTH POWER + See Oregano for vitamin, mineral and fiber health benefits. Main difference between marjoram and oregano is in their essential oils, although the effects of the oils overlap. The chemical compounds in marjoram essential oil are primarily pinene, sabinene, camphor, borneol and origanol. The oil has anti-bacterial/viral properties. It also helps ease pain, calms the mood, promotes sleep, aids digestion and lowers blood pressure. Some use it as a diuretic or expectorant. Used to treat migraines, headaches, arthritis, asthma, respiratory infections, depression, anxiety, insomnia, constipation and stress.

VITAMIN & MINERAL

Vitamins – K, A and C
Minerals – Iron, Manganese and Calcium

DISEASE PREVENTION

See oregano for disease prevention. Essential oil may help reduce the symptoms or development of arthritis, asthma, insomnia and many bacterial, viral or fungal infections.

HOW TO GROW

Wild and pot marjoram are both hardy perennials. The more flavorful sweet marjoram grows only as a semi-hardy annual in colder regions. Prefers a site with full sun. Relatively tolerant of soil types. Grows best with moisture-retaining, well-drained soil. Work in generous amount of compost or planting mix before planting in spring. Get young transplants from a nursery. Plant about 1 foot apart. If growing sweet marjoram as an annual in temperate zone, sow seeds indoors in early spring, plant outdoors after the last frost, spacing 8 inches apart. Water regularly and keep weeds away to prevent nutrient competition. Pinch main shoots often to encourage dense, bushy growth. Fresh leaves are ready to harvest from early summer until gone or winter returns. Marjoram dries or freezes well for winter use. Grows well in pots, too. Grow entire crop this way or a few to bring in for winter to have fresh leaves all year.

INSECT CONTROL

No common pests that threaten its life.

TIPS

Divide and replant perennials every three years. Herbs are excellent added to many dishes.

Melons (Cantaloupe & Honeydew)

HEALTH POWER

Cantaloupe is rich in vitamins A, C and beta-carotene. (More than 100 percent of RDA in one cup.) Vitamin A and beta-carotene essential to maintain healthy vision. Vitamin C protects circulatory and immune systems from cell-damaging free radicals and stimulates white blood cells to fight infection. (Honeydew has much less of the vitamins but similar amounts of the others.) Also contains folate, important in producing and maintaining new cells, especially during pregnancy or when healing a severe wound. Cantaloupe helps with energy by controlling metabolism of carbohydrates.

VITAMIN & MINERAL

Vitamins – A, B1 (Thiamine), B2 (Riboflavin), B3 (Niacin), B9 (Folate), B5 (Pantothenic Acid), B6 (Pyridoxine), C, E and K
Minerals – Potassium, Phosphorus, Magnesium, Calcium, Sodium, Iron, Selenium, Manganese, Copper and Zinc

DISEASE PREVENTION

Helps reduce risk of cataracts, heart disease, stroke, many cancers and promotes overall health with broad base of vitamins and minerals. Vitamin A may help prevent emphysema in smokers and those exposed to second-hand smoke.

HOW TO GROW

First cultivated in southwestern Asia and the Nile Delta. Melons grow best in hot, dry areas. Night temperatures should not go below 55°F. Melons need 3-4 months of warm weather. Do not plant until the soil has reached 65-75°F. Require full sun, complete drainage and air circulation to prevent fungal diseases. Mix in some broken-down compost to provide nutrients and improve soil structure. Avoid water build up on the surface, since melons rest on the ground during growth. A sprinkling of fish bone meal helps. Best soil pH ranges from 6.5-7. In 2.5 to 3 months they yield ripe fruit. If growing in a cooler area, start in a heated greenhouse until it gets warm enough outside. Create a small soil hill and plant two transplants per hill. If sowing seeds outdoors, plant 6-8 seeds in a 12-inch circle on each hill. Space hills 5 to 10 feet apart, depending on projected size. Mulch after onset of summer to prevent water stress if you live in very hot, dry area. Keep soil watered regularly but keep surface relatively dry. Females have swelling below the petal tube. As flowers begin to show, notice if females are aborting. Means lack of pollinating bees. If so, pick the male flower and pollinate the stigma of the female.

INSECT CONTROL

Canteloupe and honeydue susceptible to spider mites. (In some areas the cucumber beetle, too.) Seaweed spray several times during growing season helps maintain robust plant growth. If the infestation is severe, use rotenone.

TIPS

Very prone to mildew. Grow on mounds or raised beds to prevent water build up. Cantaloupe is ripe when easy to detach from the vine. Another hint to ripeness is sweet smell and softness on each end of fruit.

Mint (Peppermint)

HEALTH POWER

Many varieties of mint, all with similar health benefits. Peppermint adds little in vitamins and minerals, but phytonutrients give excellent remedies. Peppermint oil has phytonutrients that help relax smooth muscles (the muscles lining internal organs and blood vessels), which help control symptoms of dyspepsia or indigestion. Also inhibits growth of many common harmful bacteria and fungi. Research suggests the phytonutrient perillyl alcohol can stop the growth of many types of cancers. Peppermint contains phytonutrient rosmarinic acid, an antioxidant. It also blocks some chemicals of inflammatory response. Eaten in high quantities, mint is a rich source of all nutrients below and has other health benefits through antioxidant, anti-inflammatory, and anti-cancer actions. Promotes bone health and overall wellness.

VITAMIN & MINERAL

Vitamins – A, C and B9 (Folate)
Minerals – Manganese, Calcium, Iron and Magnesium

DISEASE PREVENTION

Peppermint may reduce symptoms or onset of asthma, arthritis, and cancers of the pancreas, colon, skin, lung and breast.

HOW TO GROW

Many different cultivars. Among most popular are spearmint, peppermint, apple mint, lime, chocolate, lemon and grapefruit mint. Challenge with mint is not getting it to grow but keeping it from taking over entire garden. Can make a fragrant ground cover. Hardy perennial grows in almost any soil and site condition, but prefers partial shade, rich moist soil and slightly acidic pH. Choose site with enough space to allow mint to spread without invading other garden plants. Take root cuttings in early fall. To prevent rapid mint invasion, plant mint in a container (bucket or tub) with the rim just above soil level. This keeps roots from traversing under the soil and sprouting in undesired areas. Or control spreading by planting in containers. Allow at least 2 feet between other herbs or plants. Little maintenance needed. Water during dry weather. Harvest regularly to keep under control.

INSECT CONTROL

No common pests threaten mint. Some diseases, so keep soil moist.

To have continuous winter supply, freeze in cubes or store in a box with compost.

Mustard

HEALTH POWER ➕ Mustard greens are loaded with vitamin K, which increases bone formation and decreases its breakdown (osteoclastic processes). Especially helpful for postmenopausal women. Magnesium also an important cofactor for many enzymes, some involved with bone and cartilage building. (Others keep smooth muscles relaxed, which helps asthmatics.) With some calcium, mustard greens are good for bones. Great source of vitamin A and a good source of vitamin C. Besides being a protective antioxidant, vitamin A helps maintain healthy eyesight in low light, embryonic development and immune system function by helping develop and activate red and white blood cells. Vitamin A also helps increase blood vessel dilation and decrease blood vessel spasms. Antioxidant vitamin C protects water-soluble areas from cellular damage by free radicals. Also important in synthesis of collagen (part of blood vessels), ligaments, tendons and bone formation. (May also promote healthy immune system function, but more research is needed.) Together, antioxidant vitamins A, C and E help blood vessels relax and prevent plaque buildup. Folate is involved with DNA synthesis and protein catabolism. Folate also regulates homocysteine in the blood. (At excess levels, homocysteine is linked to hardening of blood vessels, which leads to heart disease.) Folate is also essential to proper fetal development. Mustard greens have many phytonutrients (e.g. glucosinolates) that get converted to isothiocyanates. These are being researched for their ability to inhibit cancer cell growth and stimulate production of detoxifying enzymes in the liver.

VITAMIN & MINERAL ⬆ Vitamins – K, A, C, E, B9 (Folate), B6 (Pyridoxine), B2 (Riboflavin), B1 (Thiamin) and B3 (Niacin)
Minerals – Manganese, Calcium, Potassium, Copper, Phosphorus, Iron and Magnesium

DISEASE PREVENTION Mustard greens may help avoid cardiovascular disease, stroke, osteoporosis, rheumatoid and osteoarthritis, asthma, cataracts and cancers of the mouth, throat, vocal cords, esophagus, skin, lung, breast, liver, stomach, colon and prostate.

HOW TO GROW

Easy to grow and great in salads and sandwiches or as a garnish. Can grow indoors in winter and/or outdoors in spring and fall. Grows best in cool weather with full sun. Outdoors, grows best in sunny site with moist, highly fertile soil. Indoors, it does well in shallow pans or trays. For a winter sowing, place a bit of moist soil into a tray. Scatter the seeds thickly on it. Cover the seeds with a piece of paper (newspaper, magazine page, printer paper). When seeds germinate, remove paper and set in direct sunlight. When they begin to grow, put them in fertile soil. If sowing outdoors, sow in a container the same way or in the corner of a bed. Sow every couple of weeks to get continual harvest. Greens are ready for harvest in 10-20 days. Cut and enjoy, but remember to sow another tray.

INSECT CONTROL

Mustard is largely trouble free, especially indoors. If you have a persistent infestation, consult local nursery or agriculture extension office.

TIPS

Mustard is a cool weather crop. Flowers want to develop during long, warm, summer days. Remove and compost them when hot weather arrives before flower stalks appear.

Nectarines

HEALTH POWER

Nectarines have high content of carotenoids and flavonoids, including phytonutrients lutein and lycopene, both supporters of healthy vision, heart health and the fight against carcinogens. Vitamins C and A also support immune system response to unwanted bacteria, viruses and fungi. Vitamins E and A help protect skin from UV or free radical damage and helps maintain elasticity in the inner lining of blood vessels. Nectarines give a good dose of dietary fiber, which works to promote healthy digestion and nutrient absorption from food and drink. Fiber helps balance cholesterol levels and prevents buildup of bad cholesterol. Very low in total calorie content, fat free and great source of natural sugars.

VITAMIN & MINERAL ⬆	Vitamins – C, A, B3 (Niacin) and E Minerals – Potassium, Copper, Phosphorus and Manganese

DISEASE PREVENTION 🚫	Phytonutrients in nectarines help reduce risks of atherosclerosis, heart disease, macular degeneration and many cancers.

HOW TO GROW	See Peaches for growing guidelines. Cousin to the peach, nectarines are often called "beardless peach." During a break on a warm summer day, not much beats biting into a cool, juicy nectarine. Trees take 2-3 years to produce delectable fruit. Can be grown as a bush tree, fan tree or standard. Prefers sunny site with well-drained soil not overly nutrient rich. Note: If flowering occurs before pollinating insects arrive, you may need to hand pollinate from one flower to the next. Use soft-bristled paintbrush or similar device.

INSECT CONTROL ✕	See Peaches.

TIPS ✓	Needs great drainage to get nutrients and grow disease free. If soil is thicker, in addition to amending with organic matter, sprinkle a layer of broken-down bricks or sediment into the bottom of hole to help create space for draining.

Okra

HEALTH POWER ➕	Okra is a powerful source of both soluble and insoluble fiber. The soluble fiber, in the forms of gums and pectins, lowers total cholesterol, mainly LDL (the bad form). It also helps regulate digestion, which moderates spikes in blood sugar levels. Soluble fiber puts less stress on insulin producing cells and could help prevent Type II diabetes. Insoluble fibers in okra help maintain intestinal health. They bind to wastes (some of which are toxic or contain cholesterol), absorb water and keep things flowing smoothly in the intestines. They also delay absorption of glucose and promote colon health by balancing pH levels. Okra's high quality fiber helps feed beneficial bacteria in the intestines, contributing to more efficient breakdown of food and nutrient absorption. Okra's vitamin K contributes

to blood clotting and strong, healthy bones. Also low in calories, which makes it ideal for eating healthy while losing weight.

VITAMIN & MINERAL

Vitamins – C, A, B1 (Thiamin), B2 (Riboflavin), B9 (Folate), and B3 (Niacin)

Minerals – Calcium, Magnesium, Potassium, Manganese, Iron, Phosphorus, Zinc and Copper

DISEASE PREVENTION

Okra may help suppress or prevent the symptoms or onset of colon cancer, heart disease, diabetes, ulcers, and mouth and lung cancers. Vitamin C in okra is an antioxidant that helps ward off potential carcinogens and blocks cholesterol buildup. It is also anti-inflammatory and works to help prevent cataracts, atherosclerosis, asthma and arthritic conditions. Vitamin A, an antioxidant with other flavanoids, wards off carcinogens. They help the eyes, too, aiding night vision and slowing macular degeneration.

HOW TO GROW

Okra is an annual originating in the tropics. Popular in the South for thickening gumbos or stews. It grows as an upright bush that produces hibiscus-like flowers followed by five-sided pods used for eating. Okra wants full sun in moisture retaining soil with good drainage. It grows best outdoors in warmer temperatures, but you can start indoors and transplant in warm weather. Sow the seeds when temperature reaches the mid-60's. Soak for 24 hours and plant in highly fertile soil amended well with compost or planting mix. Place seeds ½ to ¾ inches deep and 3 inches apart. Thin out later to 2 feet apart. Keep about 3 feet between each row. Mulch when it is 4 inches tall to prevent weeds and hold moisture. Water okra well during dry times. Reapply organic fertilizer every month. Pods will appear 50-60 days after planting. Harvest when they are young and soft, no bigger than finger size, as they harden during maturation.

INSECT CONTROL

Pests not a big problem for very resilient okra. Stinkbugs, corn earworms, flea beetles, aphids, or cabbage loopers may be a nuisance. Pick off stinkbugs or worms when you see them. Remove aphids with a strong spray of water or introduce predators such as lady beetles, lacewings or midges. If they do not work, use garlic spray, insecticidal soap or rotenone. For flea beetles, introduce parasitic nematodes or spray with rotenone. If attacks are severe, use rotenone for all as a last resort.

Harvest daily to stimulate more pod growth and discard the firm pods that were missed or did not get harvested on time. Cook okra over low heat to maintain nutritional value.

Olives

HEALTH POWER ✚ Olives are a great source of the fat-soluble antioxidant vitamin E, which helps protect fat-based areas of the body. They also have monounsaturated fats, which resist oxidative damage by free radicals much better than poly-unsaturated fats. Olives also contain proactive phytonutrients including polyphenols and flavonoids, both having antioxidant and anti-inflammatory roles. They help protect cells from free radical damage that could lead to heart disease or colon cancer. The anti-inflammatory properties may also reduce pain or recovery time for "red and sore" conditions. Olives have iron and dietary fiber, too. The iron helps hemoglobin in the blood bind oxygen in the lungs for delivery to all tissues. Fiber promotes smooth digestion, helps lower excess cholesterol and regulates blood sugar levels.

VITAMIN & MINERAL ⬆ Vitamins – E
Minerals – Iron and Copper

DISEASE PREVENTION ⊘ Olives may help reduce the risk of developing heart disease, colon cancer, asthma, osteoarthritis and rheumatoid arthritis.

HOW TO GROW Olives grow best in areas with cool winters and warm to hot summers. They come in two main types, African and European. The African ones are inedible, but you can use them to give the yard visual appeal. European olives provide edible fruit about six years after planting but continue to bear for many years. They are also self-fertile, so one is enough for olive production. An olive tree grows as a standard tree and needs minimal pruning. For soil, they need only good drainage. For best growth, work organic matter (compost or planting mix) into the soil. They can grow, though, in lumpy or stony soil and can be good filler for an area that cannot support many other plants. Trees can be purchased container grown as transplants. Best time of year to plant is in the fall before moist weather. With more than one tree, space them about 30 feet apart. The one nutrient olives need in quantity is nitrogen, so mulch over the roots of the tree every spring with well-aged compost, manure or planting mix. If growth seems stunted, treat the soil to nutrient-dense fertilizer like compost tea, feather or kelp meal. Throughout growth, prune off branches that cause overcrowding and block sunlight from the inner foliage. Harvest olives by hand in fall when they are green. Or leave them on a bit longer into the winter until they turn black.

INSECT CONTROL ✕ Grown organically, olive trees do not usually have pest problems. Some pests stay away from olive trees because of the "chemical quality" of olive oil. Some general garden pests may cause issues. Watch for any infestations. Remove larger bugs by hand and destroy them. If uncertain about a pest, collect a few or take photographs and visit the nursery for help on identification and treatment.

TIPS ✓ Green olives are great for pickling. Black olives can also be pressed for olive oil.

Onions

HEALTH POWER + Onions have a dense collection of phytonutrients that give many health benefits. These include powerful sulfur-containing molecules like allyl propyl disulfide and a multitude of flavonoids including quercetin. Eating onions can help increase efficient processing of free-floating glucose in the body. Allyl propyl raises free-floating insulin in the blood by preventing it from becoming inactivated in the liver. Chromium also decreases blood sugar by making cells more responsive to insulin, resulting in cellular glucose uptake. Onions are also heart healthy by reducing the amount of cholesterol and homocysteine in the blood, both linked to heart problems. Quercetin is an antioxidant that benefits the colon by protecting against carcinogens. Another onion compound blocks osteoclasts (cells that break down bone), which is beneficial for elders whose bone production has slowed. Vitamin C, quercetin and isothiocyanates reduce joint swelling.

VITAMIN & MINERAL

Vitamins: C, B6 (Pyridoxine) and B9 (Folate)
Minerals – Chromium, Manganese, Molybdenum, Potassium, Phosphorus and Copper

DISEASE PREVENTION

Allyl propyl and chromium act to reduce demand for insulin, which can stave off or help manage diabetes. By lowering cholesterol, homocysteine levels and blood pressure, the vitamins (especially folate) and minerals reduce the risk of atherosclerosis, heart disease, stroke and heart attack. Eating onions regularly has also been linked with lower risk for a number of cancers: esophageal, oral cavity, pharynx, colorectal, laryngeal, breast, prostate, ovarian and kidney. The anti-inflammatory properties help deal with rheumatoid arthritis, osteoarthritis and asthma.

HOW TO GROW

Onions are great to have in the kitchen. They are versatile, store well, come in many different flavors and cook easily. Choose a site full of sunshine. Work in plenty of organic matter in the form of aged compost, manure or planting mix. Best pH is roughly 6.5; add lime to raise if needed. To save space and a few dollars, sow multiple onion seeds together. They grow next to each other and push each other over slightly to make room as they enlarge. Sow 6-7 seeds together. If you want to start early, they germinate well indoors in trays on the windowsill or under a fluorescent light. Indoors, you need to gradually accustom them to being outside before transplanting. Otherwise, sow them similarly in shallow drills roughly 1 foot apart just after spring begins. Thin seedlings to a couple inches apart. Sow the Japanese varieties toward the end of summer in the same way. Fertilize this variety in the spring to encourage the rest of growth. With onions, you must keep beds weed free to minimize nutrient and sunlight competition. Water during dry weather but not overmuch. When tops turn brown, pull or dig up bulbs and let them dry in the sun for a couple days. If weather is unpredictable, put them in shelter to dry out. Once they are dry, remove their tops, and store them in a perforated sack or net in a well-ventilated, warm, shaded place to cure and avoid rot.

INSECT CONTROL

Pests are not generally a problem with onions, especially the Allium species. Common pests include onion maggots, onion eelworm and onion flies. Attacking from early to mid-summer, the onion fly can be controlled by hoeing around each plant to expose the maggots to birds. Or put sand around the base of each plant to deter female egg laying. Alternatively, multiple sowing avoids the need to thin out the plants, which prevents releasing the attractive smell to female onion flies. Onion eelworms get inside the bulbs. The only way to get rid of them is to dig up the affected plants and replace for a couple years with something that is not a host (broccoli, lettuce, cabbage or another crucifer). If the risk of infestation is high in your location, interplant onions among other plants to give pests a smaller target to attack. A number of the Allium species ward off pests like aphids, beetles and carrot flies from other garden plants like carrots, lettuce and parsnips.

TIPS ✓ For a continual harvest, grow a main crop variety and a Japanese crop that harvests first. To avoid sun burning while waiting for onions to dry on a hot day, cover one plant's bulb with another's shoots.

Oranges & Tangerines

HEALTH POWER + Besides high vitamin C, oranges contain flavanoids under the sub-category flavanones. The flavanone herperidin, in animal studies, has shown it can lower blood pressure, cholesterol and inflammation. This flavanone and others are found mostly in the peel and pulp of the orange rather than the juice. Thus, you can be less meticulous about removing all the peel before eating. Vitamin C is vital in protecting cells in the immune system and disarming aqueous free radicals that cause cell damage (potentially carcinogenic DNA mutations). Compounds known as limonoids remain active for extended periods. Along with folate, potassium, fiber and many phytonutrients, citrus fruits are antioxidant, anti-allergenic, anti-carcinogenic and anti-inflammatory. They also help lower blood pressure, promote proper digestion and prevent kidney stones.

VITAMIN & MINERAL ⬆ Vitamins – C, Folate, B1 (Thiamin) and A
Minerals – Potassium and Calcium

DISEASE PREVENTION ⊘ Oranges help reduce the potential for a multitude of cancers: lung, colon, esophageal, mouth, pharynx, larynx and stomach. Antioxidants in vitamin C reduce effects of inflammatory conditions like asthma, osteoarthritis and rheumatoid arthritis. Phytonutrients, vitamins and minerals help reduce the risk of ulcers and atherosclerosis.

Oranges grow best in climates moderately warm year-round. Extended frost deforms or kills fruit. In cool climates, oranges must be grown in a greenhouse. Orange trees are bushy. Two types of oranges, sweet and sour. Sweet oranges are common for eating and comprise most of what is in the produce section of a grocery store. Best time for planting is spring or fall. They need as much sun as possible with as little wind as possible. This may require planting close to a fence corner, house corner or building a wind barrier. Soil should be slightly acidic; pH just above 6.0, and consist of a sandier loam with great drainage. Planting orange trees decreases soil drainage. If soil is denser, raise planting area by about 18 inches. Baby orange trees can be found at any nursery in a habitable climate. Before planting, amend the area with plenty of organic material. Plant the tree so the point at which branches converge is 4-5 inches off the ground. With multiple trees, space them about 25 feet apart to avoid nutrient competition or light deprivation. Throughout the first couple years, make sure roots get plenty of water. Be careful not to add too much chemical fertilizer, which can damage roots. Add a few fistfuls of planting mix heavy in fish bone, feather, kelp and other meals once in the spring and summer over the soil where roots are growing. During growth, if tree becomes too thick in certain areas, thin out by removing branches. Harvest when oranges have deep color. Twist off gently so as not to break off the fruit-bearing shoot. Fruits can hang ripened for up to six months. Immediately after harvesting, trim the same shoot (not branch) to roughly 5 inches to encourage more fruit-bearing shoots.

Popular outdoor pests include gall wasps. Indoor pests are aphids, scale insects and/or red spider mite. Gall wasps lay their eggs into new shoot growth in spring. Once hatched, larvae embed themselves in shoots, causing unnatural looking swellings (galls) to show up. The only way to control these creatures is to cut out galls when they appear and destroy them. Aphids prefer dry weather. They can be warded off via biological controls such as introducing ladybugs or by growing a plant like marigolds to attract them. Insecticidal soap controls a large infestation. Red spider mites, like aphids, thrive in drier temperatures. Attacks can be prevented by frequently spraying with water. If they attack heavily, a controlled spraying of rotenone gets rid of them.

Without fertilizer containing trace elements such as zinc, orange trees develop little leaf. This causes mottling of leaves and possibly deformed fruit. Avoid this by applying well-aged compost, manure or fertilizer with seaweed meal.

Oregano

HEALTH POWER

Contains the potent volatile oils thymol and carvacrol, known to have antibacterial action stronger than some prescriptions. Thymol and rosmarinic acid are effective antioxidants, helping to eliminate cell-damaging free radicals. Oregano is also a great source of some minerals and vitamins, especially vitamin K. This often-overlooked vitamin may help promote heart health by helping to keep calcium from forming plaque in arteries. It also promotes bone health and blood clotting.

VITAMIN & MINERAL

Vitamins – K, A and C
Minerals – Manganese, Iron and Calcium

DISEASE PREVENTION

The high fiber in oregano makes it a good way to reduce cholesterol, defend against colon cancer and promote healthy digestion by absorbing good nutrients and eliminating toxins. Also, omega-3 fatty acids are polyunsaturated fats that also help create the healthier HDL form of cholesterol. It may help prevent high blood pressure associated with heart disease. Oregano's essential oil helps prevent many bacterial, viral and fungal infections. It also helps digestion and calms the nerves.

HOW TO GROW

Many species of oregano, some not suitable for cooking. Watch out for O. vulgare, which has a purple flower. It is tasteless and sometimes mistakenly sold for cooking. The most aromatic and common one for cooking is O. heracleoticum or, confusingly, O. vulgare subsp. hirtum. These produce white flowers rising a foot above the leaves. Oregano is a perennial that grows best with full sunlight in well-drained soil. The low-cost way is to start from seed or get healthy labeled transplants from a good local nursery. After the last frost, loosen the soil up with garden spade. If the soil is shallow or needs some amending to help drainage, create a raised bed by mixing in some fine gravel, grit or sand. Plant the transplants outdoors 14-18 inches apart. If starting from seed, plant these 6 inches apart about 1/2 inch deep. If planting more than one row, space them out 18 inches. When seeds sprout up, thin out the plants to one foot apart. Keep the soil moist for the first couple months. After that, it tolerates dry weather and only needs water when soil dries out. As the plant grows, trim back straying stems and pinch off flower buds to encourage optimal growth and desired shape. When the plant reaches 5-6 inches tall and/or has more than a dozen leaves, harvest as needed for cooking. When the season ends, cut the plants all the way down and mulch around them before winter to insulate roots from freezing temperatures. If you have too many leaves to use, dry them in a cool, dark place, chop up and store in an airtight container.

Oregano deters some common garden pests and can be planted methodically to help protect other plants. Since we eat the leaves, if pests become a problem, avoid using chemical pesticides or sprays. Although unlikely, sometimes aphids or thirps will attack. If the problem is not serious, let the pests do a little damage rather than introduce chemicals. If needed, try an organic treatment such as insecticidal soap.

Avoid using fertilizer to promote stronger flavor in the leaves. Oregano seeds can be sown in containers and transplanted 12 inches apart after the last frost or just left to grow spaced out in containers. When harvesting, cut the leaves off in the morning just after dew recedes. They have the most flavor and aroma before the sun causes oils to move into the shoots. Replace the plant after 2-4 years when it starts to become woody. Eat fresh oregano as much as possible to get all the beneficial oils. Oregano is a great source of omega-3 fatty acids.

Parsley

In addition to great plate décor, parsley has excellent potential health benefits. It contains volatile oils such as limonene, myristicin and eugenol and beneficial flavonoids like apiin, apigenin and luteolin. The volatile oils act as anti-carcinogens (in animal studies) and may act similarly in humans. Myristicin activates an enzyme that attaches glutathione to highly reactive molecules (some are carcinogens) neutralizing them. The flavonoids have antioxidant properties and help neutralize oxygen-containing free radicals, preventing them from damaging cellular components (membranes, DNA, enzymes, etc.). Parsley is a great source of vitamins K, C and A.

Vitamin K helps maintain a healthy bone matrix and may help prevent some cancers. Vitamin C is an antioxidant protecting cells from damage in water-soluble areas all over the body. Both vitamins C and A strengthen the immune system. Folic acid renders homocysteine in the blood harmless, protecting blood vessel walls from damage.

VITAMIN & MINERAL

Vitamins – K, C and A
Minerals – Iron and others in trace amounts

DISEASE PREVENTION

Reduces risk and helps stop cell growth in lung cancer. Research suggests vitamin K helps resist liver and prostate cancer. Eating foods rich in vitamins C and A, like parsley, lowers the risk of atherosclerosis, colon cancer, diabetes and asthma. Arthritis sufferers may also gain relief by the anti-inflammatory actions of vitamins C and A. Folic acid is important for proper cellular division in both the colon and cervix, reducing the risk of those cancers. Folic acid's effect on homocysteine helps prevent cardiovascular diseases.

HOW TO GROW

Whether used as a topping or worked into a sauce, parsley puts a finishing touch on dishes. There are two main types: flat and curly leafed. Flat leafed is the pungent Italian parsley. Curly leafed is used for cooking and garnishing plates. Both are biennials and grow about 14 inches. Plant out in the spring or start them indoors, which might be better, since the seeds take a month to germinate. In either case, soak them in warm water for a few hours or over night before planting. Space seeds out about 6 inches. They grow in well-enriched fertile soil in both pots and the ground. They prefer a bit of shade. For a harvest every year, plant new parsley every spring. They are frost hardy and come back to life the second year to flower if the winter is not too harsh. If you cut off the flower stalks, they will not die in the second year. Conversely, if they flower and go to seed, they can sow themselves and need little effort to reproduce. Those able to sow themselves are healthier and taste better. Harvest the leaves as needed from the outer leaves in. Taking inner leaves first prematurely sends the parsley to seed.

INSECT CONTROL

Generally, no pest problems with parsley. Herbs attract pollinating insects, like bees, for other plants and beneficial predatory insects to control other pests.

✓ Parsley does not keep long. Either freeze it or dry it in an oven to preserve for later use. If you want to grow it during winter, sow seeds in a pot during mid-summer and bring them in just before the weather cools down. To save seeds, harvest the stems as the seeds ripen and hang them upside down over a cloth in a ventilated shed.

Parsnips

HEALTH POWER + Benefits are similar to potatoes. The main difference: parsnips have more fiber and folate but less vitamin C per weight. (Still a great source, with half the RDA of C in one parsnip.) With more dietary fiber, parsnips better support digestion. They help everything flow smoothly, get rid of excess cholesterol and regulate blood sugar. Folate is known to lower homocysteine in the blood, preventing plaque buildup that harms blood vessel structure. Pregnant women need folate to promote healthy fetal nerve development. Also a good source of vitamin K, which helps develop a dense bone matrix. Parsnips have some B vitamins that help boost fat, protein and carbohydrate metabolism to provide energy.

VITAMIN & MINERAL ↑ Vitamins – C, K, B9 (Folate), E, B1 (Thiamin), B5 (Pantothenic Acid) and B6 (Pyridoxine)
Minerals – Manganese, Potassium, Magnesium, Phosphorus and Copper

DISEASE PREVENTION ⊘ Vitamin B6 and folate help reduce homocysteine levels, helping to prevent heart attacks and strokes. Vitamin B6 also fights cancer by attaching signals to molecules that lead to turning on tumor suppressive genes. This type of signaling, methylation, also signals to destroy toxic, potentially carcinogenic, chemicals. The fiber in parsnips helps prevent colon cancer and the onset of diabetes. The fiber may also reduce the risk or onset of heart disease, stroke and heart attack.

HOW TO GROW 🌱 Parsnips grow in many different soil types. For best results, choose a sunny, sheltered site with deep soil. The pH should be around 6.5; add lime to raise, if needed. In cooler climates, sow seeds as soon as the soil starts to warm and is workable (early to mid-spring). In warmer climates that do not freeze, sow seeds in the fall. Loosen the soil to 2 feet down. Remove any large solid chunks like rocks. Amend the soil with a few inches of compost or equivalent planting mix. Soak seeds in warm water for several hours to promote germination. Create shallow drills 1 foot apart and sow seeds 1 inch deep 6 inches apart. Do not let soil dry out while waiting for germination. Mulch lightly around the base of the plants once they are a few inches tall. Hoe to keep rows weed free, making sure not to damage roots. Water deeply once a week to supply the whole root and avoid rot from sitting water. If soil dries out, water again to keep it moist and prevent cracking of roots. Parsnips take 3-4 months to mature. They are usually ready in late fall to early winter. Use a garden fork to loosen soil around plants before pulling. Lift roots after first frost. Enjoy or store for winter use.

INSECT CONTROL ✗ Common pests for parsnips are carrot root flies. They are also susceptible to canker. The larva of the female fly burrows into the root, leaving tunnels and brown marks. To prevent females from laying eggs at root base, put a plastic barrier around parsnips, carrots or celery supported by posts. This keeps females from approaching the base of the plant. Parsnips have canker if they show red-brown marks on the top of the roots, which leads to rot. To prevent, do not over water or over fertilize. Use balanced practices to develop a healthy plant. Also, look for resistant cultivars.

TIPS ✓ To store parsnips, gently place undamaged ones in a container and fill in gaps with moist peat, sawdust or sand. Put the container in a cool, frost-free area.

Peaches

HEALTH POWER + Peaches are an excellent source of vitamins A and C. Vitamin A is an antioxidant that stabilizes free radicals associated with cancer and other diseases. It also aids proper vision in low light. Vitamin C is famous for its many benefits: healing cuts and abrasions, building connective tissue for muscles and bones, protecting immune system, preventing bruising and helping build new red blood cells. Peaches also contain other vitamins and minerals, including fiber, that aid in proper digestion and help enhance skin color.

VITAMIN & MINERAL		Vitamins – A, B1 (Thiamin), B2 (Riboflavin), B6 (Pyridoxine), C, B3 (Niacin), B9 (Folate), B5 (Pantothenic Acid), C, E and K Minerals – Potassium, Phosphorus, Magnesium, Calcium, Iron, Selenium, Manganese, Copper and Zinc
DISEASE PREVENTION		The anti-oxidant glutathione, with vitamins A and C, correlates with preventing cancer cell development. Eating peaches reduces the risk of heart and cardiovascular disease.
HOW TO GROW		A gorgeous addition to the backyard, peaches work miracles in summer. They grow throughout the U.S. but do best in warm summers. They thrive in healthy, well-drained soil. Pick a transplant from your nursery and put it in a fairly sunny spot. Amend the soil with plenty of compost or organic planting mix. Plant the tree deep. The first few years set the stage for the tree's shape and size. Stake the tree after it grows taller than a foot to help it grow straight up. In spring, when growth buds appear, cut the central growth down to two feet above the ground right above the bud. Remove all the lower shoots except for the top 3-4. Later, remove any shoots under those top 3-4 branches. Before fruit bearing age, mulch widely around the trunk with compost or organic planting mix twice a year, once in March and again in May. After that, one application a year is good unless you see signs of deficiency. Keep soil moist. Water thoroughly if the soil might dry out. If soil stays too dry too long, fruiting suffers. When peaches are about cherry size, remove some, leaving 1-3 peaches per stem. If clusters form on branches, remove all but one to avoid stunting growth. When they are the size of golf balls, check the branches again and remove enough to ensure branches withstand the weight. They are ready to pick when skin softens to the touch.
INSECT CONTROL		The most serious pests are peach tree borers. Aphids and spider mites are also common. Borers enter on the lower trunk and leave sticky sawdust around their entry. Prevent by keeping the lower trunk uncovered. Kill them by sticking something in the hole such as the end of a wire coat hanger. Or cut out damaged areas until you see healthy wood. Treat with a 1:1 mix of lime-sulfur and latex paint. Aphids are a common garden pest. Control aphids by companion planting marigolds to attract their predators (hover flies or ladybugs). You can also wipe or spray off with a strong stream of water. If infestation is too great, spray an organic insecticidal soap. Red spider mites are barely visible, but their webs are easy to

see. They succeed in dry conditions, so keep plant regularly sprayed with water. For a bad infestation, spray with an organic pesticide like rotenone.

TIPS ✓ The more peaches on a tree, the smaller they are. After a few growing seasons, you can determine the size that yields the best fruit to your taste. Quickly remove any shoots emerging from the roots. Also, completely remove any infested peaches or branches damaged during the previous year. This restores vigor to branches and fruit growing. Many vitamins are in the skin, so eat peaches whole.

Pears

HEALTH POWER + Pears give a solid defense against damaging free radicals and are a great source of dietary fiber. Vitamin C and copper help keep highly reactive free radicals from causing oxidative damage to cells all over the body. Vitamin C is water-soluble and defends almost the entire body except areas of fat. It stops free radicals from oxidizing cholesterol into a sticky form that leads to plaque buildup in blood vessels. It also protects white blood cells while they fight off infection and reactivates antioxidant vitamin E. Because vitamin E is fat soluble, by activating it vitamin C helps disarm free radicals in both water-soluble areas and fat-soluble areas. Dietary fiber in pears acts to reduce cholesterol, regulate blood sugar levels and support good digestion.

VITAMIN & MINERAL ⬆ Vitamins – C and K
Minerals – Copper and Potassium

DISEASE PREVENTION 🚫 Reduced risk of colon cancer, postmenopausal breast cancer, heart disease and macular degeneration.

HOW TO GROW Make sure your pear tree suits your climate. They flower early. If frosts extend well into spring, choose a late-flowering variety. Except for flowering, they are winter hardy. Most cultivars need cross pollination to fruit properly. Plant at least two trees that flower at the same time to get fruit to set. Tree height depends on the cultivar you choose. You can find self-pollinating dwarf trees with three cultivars grafted to one rootstock. This is a good option if space is limited. Best time to plant is early spring. Choose a sunny, sheltered spot with deeper soil. Prepare the soil by amending all around planting area with well-aged compost or planting mix rich in organic matter. Be careful not to over fertilize with nitrogen. This may stimulate too much new growth vulnerable to the deadly fire blight disease. Test the soil to be sure pH is 6-6.5. If not, nutrient deficiencies can cause deformities. Dig a hole wide enough and deep enough to set the bare rooted tree so the existing soil line on the trunk matches up with ground level and roots are unobstructed. A small mound of soil in the center of the hole may help support the tree. Fill the hole with the amended soil and pack it down lightly. Mulch around stem with a thick layer of well-aged manure or compost to ensure nutrient availability. Keep the soil moist by thorough watering. No need to water every day, but make sure to water long enough to reach the root level. (Watering just the surface encourages roots to grow upward.) You can thin out clusters or leave them alone, depending on how big you want fruits to be. If you want large fruit, thin the center fruit in each cluster near mid-summer. With several clusters on a branch, the weight can make a branch break or severely warp. Avoid this by thinning clusters on these branches to one fruit per cluster. Prune thick branches that block sunlight from reaching the foliage. Each spring, spread a thin layer of organic fertilizer and mulch over the roots. Pears take 2 or more years to bear fruit. Harvest fruit when it easily detaches with a slight tug. Store in cool temperatures. Bring up to room temperature before eating to soften and sweeten them up.

INSECT CONTROL ✕ Pear tree pests are aphids, wooly aphids, winter moth, coddling moth, sawfly and wasps. Fire blight is the most common disease. Remove aphids with a strong water stream. Also, draw their predators (hoverflies and ladybugs) by planting French marigolds nearby. Wooly aphids are more difficult to remove. They form colonies on branches and cover themselves with a white waxy substance. Scrape off as soon as you see them. Or spray with rotenone after petals fall. If that does not work, cut them out. You can stop female winter moth caterpillars from breeding on the lower trunk by securing a sticky ring around the tree to catch them as they crawl up to lay eggs. Coddling moths lay eggs that hatch into fruit maggots. Deter them with a pheromone trap hung from a branch. (Find at your local nursery.) Sawfly quickly eat leaves off. Spray with an insecticide when you see caterpillars on leaves. If wasps are a problem, make a trap by putting sweet liquid in a container covered with a thin layer that has a hole in it. Hang this from the tree. Wasps will enter the container and be trapped. For fire blight, find out if your area is susceptible and buy a resistant cultivar. Otherwise, don't prune too much as new soft growth is most susceptible.

TIPS ✓ When fruit stops growing and starts changing color, stop watering to keep the tree free of diseases. Pear trees grow tall but can be easier to harvest if shaped correctly.

Peas

HEALTH POWER ✚ Green peas promote overall health with seven vitamins, eight minerals and other phytonutrients. Vitamin K, crucial for bone health, is most abundant in peas. Some of it converts to vitamin K2 and is part of bone mineralization. Deficiency in K2 hinders mineralization and makes osteoporosis more likely. Incompletely researched, folate and vitamin B6 may contribute to bone health by blocking the buildup of homocysteine, a molecule that interrupts proper bone matrix formation. Vitamin K and folate also help the cardiovascular system. Vitamin K is essential for blood clotting, while folate and vitamin B6 lower homocysteine, which may reduce damage to arterial walls and reduce the risk of cardiovascular disease. Green peas also contain B vitamins that help break down carbohydrates, fats and proteins for energy. Iron is crucial for blood cell formation and oxygen delivery to muscles. Vitamins C and A protect many types of cells in the eye, liver, immune system, adrenal glands, connective tissue and the circulatory system.

VITAMIN & MINERAL ⬆ Vitamins – K, C, B1 (Thiamin), B9 (Folate), A, B6 (Pyridoxine), B3 (Niacin) and B2 (Riboflavin)
Minerals – Manganese, Phosphorus, Magnesium, Copper, Iron, Zinc and Potassium

DISEASE PREVENTION ⊘ Green peas are linked with reducing cell damage that causes osteoporosis, lymphoma, leukemia, and cancers of the lung, colon, cervix, breast, prostate and ovary. Eating green peas regularly with other nutrient-rich fruits and veggies promotes overall health and helps prevent many adverse health conditions.

HOW TO GROW

Peas are one of the oldest cultivated vegetables. Eating them fresh, right after picking, makes a big difference in flavor. Peas do not need much done to the soil for healthy growth. They produce their own nitrogen and need very little fertilizer. Peas are frost hardy, but do not deal well with heat. They slow down when temperatures go above 70°F and stop growing above 75°F. Early varieties will do well in sandier loam that warms up quickly. Later varieties may benefit from heavier soil to keep them cool. Pick a sunny spot for early varieties and part shade for later varieties. Make sure soil is well drained. Sow seeds outdoors in early spring and also in fall for mild climates. Make successive sowings to get a continuous yield. Seeds should be planted in drills 2 inches deep and roughly 2 inches apart. If planting a vine type, plant in double rows spaced 6-8 inches apart with roughly 3 feet between each double row. Support each plant with a stick roughly 4-5 feet long. Keep soil moist, but make sure not to over water. Harvest (2-3 weeks after blossoming) as close to cooking as possible.

INSECT CONTROL

Common pea pests are birds, pea moths, mice, pea and bean weevils and aphids. To deter birds, install netting around the crop. (If you don't mind, sacrifice a little bit of the yield.) Pea moths lay larvae (maggots) on plants during flowering. If attack is severe, dust with rotenone. Use this as a last resort, as rotenone kills beneficial insects. See your local nursery for pheromone traps. Mice are not usually a big problem, but cats are great to have around if they are. Pea and bean weevils are not a problem unless they attack seedlings. Dust sparingly with rotenone. Spray aphids with strong stream of water or plant marigolds to attract ladybugs.

TIPS

Mulching between rows with well-aged compost or manure helps hold moisture, deter weeds and nourish the plant, especially if soil is depleted. Pea vines are very sensitive, so handpick weeds if needed.

Peppers

HEALTH POWER

All peppers are a great source of vitamins A and C, which eliminate cell-damaging free radicals. Vitamin A also counters the effects of cigarette smoke, which may help prevent lung conditions such as emphysema. Bell peppers have the B vitamins folate and pyridoxine. Both decrease homocysteine in the blood, blocking the start of a process linked with higher cholesterol and risk of heart attack or stroke. Fiber in bell peppers helps maintain healthy heart function by lowering harmful cholesterol. Bell peppers also have a carotenoid lycopene and beta-cryptoxanthin, all linked to lower risk of many cancers when eaten regularly.

VITAMIN & MINERAL

Vitamins – C, A, B6 (Pyridoxine), K, B9 (Folate), B1 (Thiamin) and E
Minerals – Molybdenum, Manganese, Potassium and Copper

DISEASE PREVENTION

The antioxidant properties of vitamins C and A suppress or prevent the symptoms of atherosclerosis, heart disease, vascular damage, both osteoarthritis and rheumatoid arthritis, emphysema, macular degeneration and the airway swelling of asthma. Regularly eating bell peppers may reduce the risk of cancers of the bladder, prostate, pancreas, lung and cervix.

HOW TO GROW

Peppers are easier to grow than eggplant in cooler climates, but are not frost hardy and do best in warmer areas. They have two main subdivisions, sweet (bell) and spicy (chili). Hundreds of varieties to choose from. The best for your area depends on climate and soil conditions. All peppers prefer warmer climates with lengthy summers. Some are specially bred to handle cooler climates with a cover. Choose a spot with full sunlight. The soil pH needs to be just above 6. In cooler areas, warm up the soil a couple of weeks before sowing by covering the plot with plastic. If starting from seed, sow in a greenhouse or under a fluorescent light. Get them ready for planting outside by gradually exposing them to outside air, starting with just daytime, until they are fully exposed day and night. You need a cold frame to do this, which is a shallow box outdoors with an air-tight framed glass/plastic lid that can be lifted up to expose plants. Or you can get acclimatized transplants from a trusted local nursery. Amend the soil with nutrient-rich planting mix, aged compost or manure. In warm climates with no late spring frosts, plant outdoors 2 feet apart. In cooler climates, cover plants with a frost-proof perforated plastic, called a cloche. Pinch the growing end when the plants reach roughly 6 inches and attach them to a skinny rod for support. Tie side shoots for when they grow out to help support the weight of peppers. Water as regularly as it takes to keep the soil moist as they grow. Apply a liquid fertilizer rich in micronutrients every other week. Harvest the peppers after they plump up. Red and green peppers are of the same variety. You can pick them when they are green or wait a little for them to turn red. With others, harvest when plump and hold a nice deep color. Hot peppers can be refrigerated, frozen or dried in the sun to store for winter usage.

✕ Most damaging are aphids, spider mites, slugs and the white fly. See Artichokes for slug and aphid control. See Strawberries for red spider mite control. The white fly sucks the sap off many plants. Like other flies, they are attracted to the color yellow. To get rid of them, hang a thick piece of yellow paper or plastic with a thin coating of grease, or use old-style fly-paper. Make sure to prevent it from attaching to the plants.

TIPS ✓ If you are de-seeding many hot peppers to save seeds or to cook, protect your hands with gloves and make sure not to touch your eyes until after thorough washing. Capsaicin is the powerful molecule that causes the burning sensation of pepper. It is insoluble in water and stays bound to the tongue no matter how much water is used to wash it down. Milk and cheese can break capsaicin's bond with tongue receptors if it gets too hot. These varieties will grow in cooler climates: Bell (sweet) pepper: Corona, Canape, Golden Summit, Sweet Banana, Yolo Wonder, Perma Green and Merrimack Wonder. Chile (hot) pepper: Hungarian Wax (hot banana peppers) and Czechoslovakian Black. For warmer climates: Bell (sweet) peppers: Cubanelle, Pimento, Aconcagua and World Beater. Chile (hot) pepper: Cayenne, Anaheim, Jalapeno, Pablano, Serrano, Black Cuban, Holiday Cheer and the very hot Chiltepin.

Persimmons

HEALTH POWER + Persimmons are an excellent source of vitamins A and C, dietary fiber and manganese. Vitamins A and C help strengthen the immune system, maintain healthy vision and defend the body against harmful free radicals. Some notable antioxidant properties help reduce inflammation, prevent plaque buildup in blood vessels and maintain the elasticity of the inner lining of organs that have epithelial cells. Their excellent fiber promotes digestive efficiency and helps prevent the buildup of bad (LDL) cholesterol. They are also noted for their tannins, proanthocyanidins and other phytonutrients including beta-carotene, lycopene, lutein, zeaxanthin, cryptoxanthin, catechins, gallocatechins, betulinic acid and shibuol. All act as protective antioxidants throughout the body. Shibuol is a double-edged sword, however, because it can cause globs to form in the digestive tract. For this reason, wait for persimmons to ripen, and do not eat astringent varieties on an empty stomach. The tannin concentration of shibuol is very low in soft, ripened persimmons. Eating them with food in the stomach mixes them in, and they react less with stomach acids. Proanthocyanidins in the skin are linked to helping metabolic processes within cells, preventing unnecessary blood clots from forming, protecting blood vessel cells from hardening and lowering blood pressure. The nutrient content and value of a persimmon depends on which cultivar you choose and how healthy it develops. For its high antioxidant content, this is a promising fruit for overall health.

VITAMIN & MINERAL

Vitamins - A, C, B6 (Pyridoxine) and E
Minerals - Manganese

DISEASE PREVENTION

In addition to protective vitamins, the phytonutrients work in slightly separate ways, which may contribute to an overall lower risk for many cancers, macular degeneration, hypertension, cardiovascular disease and diabetes. Also, cigarette smoke can deplete the body of vitamin A. Persimmons are a great source of vitamin A and may help prevent or forestall emphysema.

HOW TO GROW

American persimmon trees, growing about 40 feet high, produce smaller fruits than Asian varieties and can tolerate brief periods of temperatures down to −20°F. Asian persimmons grow larger fruit on shorter trees (about 30 feet high) but can tolerate temperatures only down to 0°F. Get a cultivar from a trusted local nursery that can guide you on a particular variety suited for your area. They are self-fertile, but bear more fruit if you grow more than one tree. Both varieties prefer a lot of sun. Early spring is great for planting. Before planting, prepare the soil by digging a big hole and amending the dug up soil as well as some of the surrounding soil with fertile organic matter, such as compost or planting mix. Adding compost tea or manure tea is smart when planting fruit trees. Plant bare root trees in a hole big enough so that the roots are free and the soil line on the trunk matches the ground level. Fill in the hole with the amended soil and pack down. The compost mulch provides plenty of nutrients for healthy growth. A small application of fertilizer once a year helps. Give Asian persimmons a little shelter by planting near a house or other trees. You may need to stake in a windy area. Space them about 20 feet apart if you plan to grow more than one. Persimmons need little pruning. If you want to control the size, prune every spring before buds form. Since persimmons produce fruit on new wood, pruning back old wood encourages new growth and leads to more fruit. When trimming, train the tree to grow around a central leading shoot that grows roughly straight up. Trim down desired shoots to the outward growing branch they grew from. Persimmons usually ripen for harvest in early to mid-autumn. Clip off the fruit when it's still firm. Let the astringent varieties soften fully before eating.

INSECT CONTROL ✗

Persimmons are pest free and tolerant in the home garden. Check with the nursery to see if your area has pests to watch for. Sometimes citrus mealy bug, borers, Psylla and scale can be a problem. Growing a tree in healthy, highly fertile soil is the best way to defend against most pests and diseases. Psylla are invisible to the eye but excrete a visible honeydew that enables a black mold to grow on the foliage. If you notice these symptoms and find the insects on inspection with a lens, or if the leaves at the top of the tree begin to turn black, spray with an insecticidal soap that has rotenone or other recommended treatment. Mealy bugs look like little white furs and live underneath leaves or stems. If noticed, spray with an insecticidal soap. Borers will enter into the lower trunk or injured limbs. If you see gooey sawdust next to a small hole, probe up into the hole to kill the borer. If the hole is on the lower trunk, close it off with paraffin or putty. If on an injured limb, remove the limb and seal off with the same material. If scale appears, spray with a copper fungicide and dispose of the leaves after they fall.

TIPS ✓

Persimmons produce many root suckers. Remove them on sight. Mulching over the root area helps deter them. Never eat unripe, astringent persimmons. They have chemicals inside that can lead to stones and intestinal disruption. Also, choose a young persimmon tree with a relatively small taproot, which transplants better. Ask the nursery about the persimmon's astringency.

Pistachio Nut

HEALTH POWER

Pistachios are packed with great overall nutrition including phytosterols, polyphenols, other antioxidants (some carotenoids), vitamins, minerals and fiber. They are one of the best nuts to get all of these nutrients, especially since they are low-fat. What they do have is "good fat," the unsaturated fats (mono- and polyunsaturated). The nutrients in pistachios make them a heart-smart snack. They are rich in the amino acid arginine, which in moderate concentrations can help relax blood vessels. The vitamins B6, B12 and folate reduce elevated levels of homocysteine, known to damage blood vessels when too high. The nut's potassium helps bring down high blood pressure and maintain proper muscle and nerve function (especially valuable for the heart). The antioxidants protect water-soluble and fat-soluble areas of the body, especially in preventing the oxidation of cholesterol. When oxidized, cholesterol becomes "sticky" and more easily adheres to artery walls, leading to plaque buildup. Antioxidants also protect against oxidative damage to DNA. Since DNA is used continuously to create new proteins, we need to protect it against "corruption" leading to mutation and loss of proper function. Fiber provides many key benefits. It promotes smooth digestion, helps expel potentially toxic substances faster and regulates blood sugar and cholesterol levels. Fiber also gives a quick, long-lasting satisfied feeling that leads to eating less often. Pistachios are a rich source of phytosterols, known to decrease the absorption of cholesterol by 30-40 percent and lower serum cholesterol in the blood. Pistachios may promote visual health from their high carotenoid content. They are also a great source of minerals that serve as cofactors for activating enzymes.

VITAMIN & MINERAL

Vitamins – B6 (Pyridoxine), B1 (Thiamin), K, B9 (Folate), E, B2 (Riboflavin), B3 (Niacin) and B5 (Pantothenic Acid)
Minerals – Copper, Manganese, Phosphorus, Magnesium, Potassium and Iron

DISEASE PREVENTION

Eating pistachios regularly may help reduce the symptoms and risk of atherosclerosis, cardiovascular disease, macular degeneration, constipation, diabetes, colon cancer and possibly many other cancers.

Pistachios love a dry warm climate like that by the Mediterranean Sea. They grow to 20-25 feet. In nature, pistachio trees have the male and female flower on separate trees, but for home gardens, nurseries have grafted female trees with male branches such that only one tree is necessary to produce nuts. If planting more than one tree, space them 20 feet or more apart. Pistachio trees take a number of years before they begin to bear heavily. After the fifth year, they bear a little. It takes another 10 years to reach full maturity and full productivity. Time to plant is in the spring. Buy a grafted cultivar adapted to your area from a local nursery. In general, they grow best in areas with cool winters and long, hot summers. They are thoroughly drought resistant. Pistachios need a site with full sun and deep soil with excellent drainage. Work in a modest amount of all-around planting mix rich in organic matter and nutrients. Taking care not to disturb the grafting point, dig a wide hole and set the tree down inside so that when filled in the soil will just cover the root crown. Water deeply more frequently when they are young. Once established, water only occasionally. The fruits are a dark red color and grow in clusters like grapes on the branches. During harvest time, the fruit husk surrounding the shell will loosen and release the nuts. Lay a sheet underneath the tree to catch them as they fall.

Pistachios are safe from pests. Consult with a nursery, and pick a cultivar that resists common infections in your area.

You may have to shake the tree to release the ripe nuts. Let them to dry for 1-2 days. They store well for months in a sealed container in a dark, cool spot.

Plums

Plums are known for a unique group of phytonutrient phenols called neochlorogenic and chlorogenic acid. These phenols help prevent oxidative damage to fats all over the body. They also disarm the free radical superoxide, which is highly reactive and can cause major damage to cells all over the body. Plums increase the absorption of iron, the mineral needed to form hemoglobin, which transports oxygen to every cell. Plums offer a nice dose of dietary fiber to promote healthy digestion. They are also a good source of vitamins A and B2, which contribute to vision, blood vessel health and metabolism of lipids, carbohydrates and sugars for energy.

VITAMIN & MINERAL

Vitamins – C, A, B2 (Riboflavin)
Minerals – Potassium and others in trace amounts

DISEASE PREVENTION

Eating fruits and vegetables high in vitamins C and A has been linked to lower risk of atherosclerosis, heart disease, stroke, asthma, colon cancer, osteoarthritis and rheumatoid arthritis.

HOW TO GROW

Plums come in many different sizes, shapes, colors and flavors. There's a type right for everyone. Some trees grow nearly 20 feet tall. You can also find dwarfs growing as small as 6 feet. You can let them be, with minimal pruning, or train them to grow as fans or pyramids. You can decide on the tree shape, how much fruit to harvest and how much area to devote to it. Plums like deep, heavier loam soils that have good drainage and a pH near 6.5. Plant plum trees in spring. Dig a deep hole and amend the soil with plenty of organic matter (compost, planting mix or a combination of nutrient rich organic matter with fertilizer). Drive a support down into the hole. When placing the tree into the hole, line up the soil line on the tree with the ground surface. Fill in the hole with the amended soil, pack it down and mulch around the trunk with a thick layer to conserve moisture and deter grass and weeds. Attach the support with a tree collar that will not erode the tree, making it prey to silver leaf disease. With standard cultivars, leave at least 20 feet between trees. With dwarf varieties, 12 feet is enough. Keep the soil moist but not water logged. It takes 3-4 years after planting to bear fruit. Each spring, reapply planting mix to the soil and mulch over the area of root growth with well-aged compost to provide all the macro- and micronutrients needed. Thin small fruits to about 2 inches apart and 4 inches between large ones. During growing season, prune off extra thick growth that blocks sunlight from the interior so fruits can properly ripen. Over winter, prune off old wood to stimulate new growth. Harvest plums for cooking just before they soften. Or pick them off as they soften.

INSECT CONTROL

Pests attacking plums are plum sawfly, wasps, red spider mite, aphids and birds. Deter aphids with a strong stream of water or by planting French marigolds to attract their predators, ladybugs and hoverflies. See Apricots for spider mites, sawflies and birds. If wasps become a problem, put something sweet in a jar (beer, juice, cider) and cover it with a film. Put a small hole in the cover and hang it from the tree. Wasps will be attracted, crawl inside the jar and get trapped.

TIPS ✓ When watering, do it long enough for water to penetrate to the root level. Otherwise the roots will try to grow toward the surface for hydration. Also, never prune plums during the winter, as the wounds will remain open and susceptible to silver leaf.

Pomegranate

HEALTH POWER + Pomegranates have many vital vitamins and minerals. They also contain polyphenols, tannins, anthocyanins and ellagic acid, all highly beneficial phytonutrients that lower the risk of many diseases. All act as antioxidants, helping disarm damaging free radicals as they form. Most valuable, these phytonutrients might inhibit the initiation/growth of cancer cells. They also help the immune system with antibacterial, anti-viral and anti-inflammatory properties. Pomegranates also help thin the blood, increasing blood flow, oxygen delivery to tissues and exchange of compounds to and from organs. Thinning blood and donating antioxidants prevents cholesterol from being converted into a sticky form that begins the process of plaque buildup. The polyphenols and folate help protect and maintain elasticity in the blood vessels, which lightens the pumping load on the heart. Pomegranates are one of the richest sources of dietary fiber among fruits, promoting smooth digestion, regulating blood sugar and lowering high cholesterol. Research shows that pomegranates contain a phytonutrient capable of blocking an enzyme that breaks down cartilage in humans and other animals.

VITAMIN & MINERAL ↑ Vitamins – K, C, B9 (Folate), B1 (Thiamin), B5 (Pantothenic Acid), B3 (Riboflavin) and E
Minerals – Copper, Potassium, Manganese, Phosphorus, Magnesium and Zinc

DISEASE PREVENTION ⊘ Pomegranate is a promising fruit to eat for reducing the risk of heart disease, atherosclerosis, rheumatoid and osteoarthritis and cancers of the breast, lung, prostate and colon.

HOW TO GROW Native to the Middle East, these specialty fruits add beauty to the landscape with their glossy green leaves and glowing giant red-orange flowers. They are well adapted to many climates, but need a hot, dry summer for fruits to ripen. Plant them in deep soil with great drainage in a sunny site sheltered from strong winds. They will naturally develop into a bush or a small tree up to 15 feet tall and 10 feet wide. They can also be pruned as a hedge to conform to the shape of the yard or to look pretty. Planting from both seed and cuttings are the most popular methods. If you already have a pomegranate tree, cut off one of the suckers and transplant it as a cutting. Sow seeds after the first frost in the spring and/or plant cuttings in warmer weather (late spring to summer). You can get pomegranate cuttings 1-2 feet long in February or March. Work in compost or planting mix rich in organic matter and nutrients. Plant them so that 2/3 of the cutting is covered in soil. When the plant is young, water more often (every two days) to stimulate growth and help it get established. Once growth accelerates, and the tree sets a solid root foundation (about 2 months), give one deep watering every couple of weeks. Fertilize twice a year (once in early spring and fall) to help the plant grow strong, hardy and insect resistant. If you plant from cuttings, the tree should bear after 3 years. You may get a few in the season before. Harvest when they are the correct ripe color for the variety you are growing (ranging from purple and red to pink).

INSECT CONTROL ✕ Pomegranates usually are unaffected by pests or diseases that threaten yields in the home garden. Aphids are the most common but rarely leave damage behind unless the infestation is large and resilient. Monitor your plants. If aphids come, spray them off with a strong stream of water. Or plant French marigolds to attract their predators (ladybugs and hover flies) which eat aphids by the thousands. If something else comes up, photograph the pest and see your local nursery or agricultural extension office.

TIPS ✓ Check with the nursery to see which cultivar is best suited to grow in your area. Remember, they need a hot, dry summer for fruit to ripen. Watch for shoots growing up from the base of the trunk. These are suckers and should be pruned and discarded or replanted

Potatoes

HEALTH POWER

Potatoes are wrongly maligned as a high-carbohydrate starch with little or no nutritional value. Not so. The "problem" with potatoes is how they are often prepared (deep fried in oil) and/or what people put on them (high-fat dairy products and/or bacon bits). Potatoes have many different vitamins and phytonutrients. A crucial one is Vitamin B6, which helps build new cells and assists proper signaling in the brain. B6 also helps give us energy by breaking down carbohydrates during exercise. It also has fiber that helps lower cholesterol and supports digestion.

VITAMIN & MINERAL

Vitamins – B6 (Pyridoxine) and C
Minerals – Potassium, Copper and Manganese

DISEASE PREVENTION

Vitamin B6 helps control homocysteine, which helps prevent heart attacks or strokes by keeping vessel walls flexible and free of plaque. It also fights cancer development by attaching signals to molecules that turn on tumor suppressor genes. This type of signaling is called methylation and also serves as a signal to destroy toxic chemicals. The fiber in potatoes helps prevent indigestion and colon cancer.

HOW TO GROW

One of the cheapest, easiest foods to find at your local market. But most places offer only a few choices. Grow them yourself and choose among many different kinds. You can also enjoy a fresher, more flavorful 'tater.' With so many varieties, choose a few different types to find those that grow and taste best to you. If you buy seeds, get those certified disease-free. You can also create them yourself by saving the strongest, healthiest ones from a shop or your garden. When making potato seeds, place potatoes with the eye face-up adjacent to each other in a container in a cool room with plenty of air and light. After 4-5 weeks, they will be bright green and sprout. Discard the thinner, smaller sprouts (risk of disease) and keep the bigger, bushier ones. If they have more than one sprout, cut them into a few pieces before planting. Choose a sunny, warm, sheltered area. Amend the soil well with nitrogen-rich planting mix and/or compost. The soil needs to drain well or the tubers will rot. Cover the dedicated area with polypropylene to protect youngsters from weeds and frost. Cut slits in plastic and plant them a couple weeks before the last frost with sprouts facing up about 8 to 10 inches deep, a foot apart. Rows should be 2-3 feet apart. If shoots come up before frosting ends, work a bit of soil over them. When shoots grow about 10 inches above soil, work a fistful of high nitrogen plant mix like bone meal or seaweed meal along each meter of each row. Then pull soil almost to the tips of each shoot. Do this again later if the above ground growth is not very close to each other within the rows. For smaller, sweeter tubers, harvest only as they flower by cutting foliage and digging them up from the side with a garden fork. Store clean, blemish-free ones and use others right away. If you want larger mature potatoes, wait until the stems of the vines start to die back before harvest. Potatoes are also great for growing in large pots. Use the same method except start with the pot half full and add amended soil as the stem grows.

INSECT CONTROL ✕

Potatoes are affected by slugs, wireworms, cyst nematodes, leaf hoppers and many other diseases. Remove slugs by hand on moist evenings or mornings. Beer traps work as well. Start the growing season as early as possible to get the tubers well developed before pests arrive. As a general method, apply organic insecticide/fungicidal soap to prevent many pests and the development of common diseases like early blight, late blight, scab, dry rot and silver scurf. Powdering the roots with sulfur before planting also helps prevent bacterial rots.

TIPS ✓

Eat the skin! Most of the vitamins and minerals are in the tissue just below the surface. To prevent rot, dig a slightly deeper trench and line it with a little mulch first. Do not let tubers see sunlight or they will develop a toxic alkaloid. Monitor the foliage closely for signs of pests or diseases, and apply proper treatment right away.

Pumpkin

HEALTH POWER +

We most often see the seeds of large pumpkins around Halloween in late October, but they are full of important nutrients all year round. Ongoing research suggests pumpkin seeds help in maintaining prostate health. (Components in the oil prevent the enlargement caused by over-stimulation from the male hormones testosterone and dihydrotestosterone.) Pumpkin seeds also contain carotenoids and omega-3 fatty acids, which have antioxidant action and are beneficial fats compared to saturated fats. Pumpkin seeds also have magnesium and zinc, two minerals important for calcium uptake and bone building, among other benefits. The seeds are being investigated as potent anti-inflammatory agents. Animal studies show they reduce inflammation without the undesired side effects of fat damage in joint linings. Perhaps most exciting about eating pumpkin seeds: They are rich in phytosterols, molecules thought to lower cholesterol and boost the immune system. More research is needed to be conclusive, but they may also help lower the risk of some cancers.

VITAMIN & MINERAL

Vitamins – K
Minerals – Manganese, Magnesium, Phosphorus, Iron, Copper and Zinc

DISEASE PREVENTION

Regularly eating pumpkin seeds may reduce the symptoms or onset of osteoporosis, rheumatoid and osteoarthritis, anemia and other conditions (depending on the results of current research).

HOW TO GROW

See Winter Squash for how to grow. These round orange fruits, closely related to winter squash, are common for pies, seeds and Halloween décor.

INSECT CONTROL

See Summer/Winter Squash for how to manage pests.

TIPS

Pumpkins can grow large. Make sure you allow enough space for your chosen variety. Pumpkins grow on one main vine with secondary vines coming off. Tertiary vines grow off the secondary vines, and the pattern continues unless controlled. The most popular pruning method is the "Christmas tree" method. Prune the main vine when it reaches 10 feet past the last fruit you want. Prune tertiary vines when they begin to grow from buds on secondary vines, and pinch off secondary vines when they reach about 10 feet. This promotes fruit growth while limiting plant growth. Pinch off any new growth from the pruned sections. Cover vines with soil to promote secondary root growth. Rotate pumpkins once in a while to maintain symmetry, but be careful not to damage the vine.

Quince

HEALTH POWER ✚ Quince is a great source of vitamin C and a good source of fiber, potassium and iron. Due to the high pectin content, it is rarely eaten raw. Rather, it is popular for making special jams and, since it holds shape well, is popular for baking, stewing or poaching as a dessert. Rich in fiber, quince aids digestion and lowers elevated blood sugar and cholesterol. Vitamin C helps protect cells (including blood vessel and immune cells) from oxidative damage by free radicals. This makes the immune and circulatory systems function more efficiently and helps maintain the body's biochemical balance. Some studies suggest the phytonutrients (phenolics) in quince have anti-viral properties.

VITAMIN & MINERAL ⬆ Vitamins – C
Minerals – Copper, Potassium and Iron

DISEASE PREVENTION 🚫 Quince may help treat or lower the risk of heart disease, arthritis, constipation, dysentery and gastric ulcers.

HOW TO GROW 🐛 Cousin to the pear, quince needs a moderate climate much like peaches to set fruit. Depending on variety, size will range from a large shrub to a small tree. They produce large, beautiful flowers in spring. Flowering a bit later than pears, the risk of frost damage is lower. Quinces take roughly 4 years for a light harvest. After 8 years, the harvest reaches full potential and can be quite large. You can find them in the local nursery in bare rooted form or propagated by cuttings of suckers from other quince plants. They are self-fertile; only one is needed for fruit production. They prefer a sunny site and heavier soil with a pH of 6-6.5 on a slight slope for good drainage. Work in a modest amount of plant mix to the site. Plant the tree and scatter a couple handfuls per square meter of planting mix over the root zone. Mulch over where roots will grow, keeping mulch at least 1 foot from the trunk. Water more frequently at first to get established. When watering, keep going until water reaches deep into the soil. This prevents roots from wanting to grow upward and protects them from drying out. Each spring reapply a couple handfuls of plant mix to encourage growth. Quinces are ripe when they are full yellow color and begin to smell sweet. Harvest and use immediately or store in a cool dry place.

Common pests for quince include aphids, wooly aphids, winter moth, coddling moth, sawfly and wasps. Remove aphids with a strong spray of water or by companion planting French marigolds, which attracts hover-flies and ladybugs that prey on aphids. Wooly aphids are more difficult. They are hard to treat with sprays, because they cover themselves in a white waxy layer. As soon as you see these layers, scrape them off. If that fails, spray with a strong stream of rotenone after flowers have fallen. As a last resort, cut them out. Cover excess bare wood. Female winter moths have no wings and crawl up the tree to lay eggs in fall and spring. The best way to stop them is to tie a sticky band around the lower trunk during egg laying seasons. Coddling moths lay their eggs directly on the fruit, which give rise to tiny grubs that burrow directly into the fruit. Use a pheromone trap to control. Sawfly do damage as small brown caterpillars. As soon as you see them, spray with an insecticide like Bt, pyrethrum, or quassia. Wasps can be deterred by hanging a jar full of a sweet liquid (cider, stale beer, fruit juice) with a perforated top just big enough for the wasp to crawl in. Before taking these precautionary steps, ask the nursery which pests are most threatening in your area.

Throughout growth, cut out the old wood and thin the long branches to encourage lateral growth. Remove the suckers that pop up from the base.

Radicchio

The most significant nutrient in radicchio is vitamin K followed by phytonutrients like anthocyanins. Often overlooked, vitamin K plays an important biochemical role in blood clotting and bone matrix building. It is needed for the activation of many proteins in the clotting process. The overall biochemical processes require more research, but thus far vitamin K appears to help encourage the formation of bone matrix (osteoblastic processes), while discouraging the breakdown of bone (osteoclastic processes). Responsible for the deep red color, anthocyanins are promising phytonutrients that have anti-inflammatory properties and inhibit the growth of pre-malignant cancer cells, induce apoptosis (programmed cell death) in cancer cells, inhibit angiogenesis (the growth of new blood vessels that feed tumors) and reduce cancer-causing DNA damage.

VITAMIN & MINERAL	↑	Vitamins – K, B9 (Folate), C and E Minerals – Copper, Manganese and Potassium
DISEASE PREVENTION	🚫	Early research suggests radicchio may help reduce the risk of osteoporosis, hemophilia and many types of cancers.
HOW TO GROW	🌱	With its white-veined, deep red-purple leaves, radicchio is a great fall/winter veggie to add to a salad. Best time for planting is in late spring to early summer or late summer to early fall, depending on regional weather averages. The color and flavor of leaves develops in the transition to cooler temperatures. It may take a trial run to decide which one you like better. Radicchio prefers a sunny site with highly fertile moisture-retentive soil at a pH of 6.5. Amend the soil with a generous amount of aged compost or planting mix. Sowing seeds too early may cause the plants to run to seed. Start in late spring. Sow the seeds densely ¼ inch deep in shallow drills spaced about 1 foot apart. Later, thin the seedlings out to 9-10 inches apart. Keep the beds weed free and the soil moist, not soggy. If you let it dry out, they might become bitter. Right after first frost, remove outer leaves, leaving the curled interior leaves. Frost sweetens the leaf. Continue to keep the bed weed free and the soil moist. The colors should darken, and a head should begin to plump as weather cools. When the head gets plump and firm, they are ready for cutting.
INSECT CONTROL	✕	Radicchio is insect resistant but may be bothered by slugs and snails. To trap them, embed a cup of beer into the soil so that the rim is flush with the soil. Snails and slugs are attracted to the beer, slide in, get stuck and drown. For other problems, ask your local nursery what might affect radicchio in your area.
TIPS	✓	When watering, soak the soil, not the foliage. This prevents any type of rotting.

Radishes

HEALTH POWER	+	Like some other popular fruits and vegetables, radishes offer a substantial dose of vitamin C. Much research has been done on vitamin C's effects on

the immune system, but whether it plays a significant role is disputed. Vitamin C is an effective antioxidant molecule that works in the water-soluble portions of the body to disarm free radicals. Vitamin C helps reduce oxidative stress on blood vessels in the cardiovascular system (leading to plaque buildup) and lung cells. The anti-oxidants also deter free radicals from damaging plasma membranes and DNA, which may help prevent cancer-causing mutations. Vitamin C also works with an antioxidant compound, glutathione peroxidase, to help restore the activity of vitamin E (a fat-soluble vitamin). Vitamin C is an important part of collagen formation involved with healthy bone, skin and connective tissues. Radishes have phytonutrients that help aid digestion (by encouraging bile flow) and stimulate the liver to produce detoxifying enzymes that remove harmful chemicals in the blood. Radishes, both red and daikon, have the phytonutrient myrosinase, which acts as an enzyme to break down other phytonutrients in radishes (glucosinolates) to isothiocyanates. Ongoing research with isothiocyanates suggest these compounds may have strong anti-cancer properties.

| **VITAMIN & MINERAL** | ⬆ | Vitamins – C, B9 (Folate), B6 (Pyridoxine) and B2 (Riboflavin)
Minerals – Potassium and Manganese |

| **DISEASE PREVENTION** | 🚫 | Regular eating of radishes may help reduce the symptoms or development of atherosclerosis, cardiovascular disease, cataracts, kidney stones and many types of cancers. |

| **HOW TO GROW** | ☙ | Radishes are a fast-maturing root to grow between slower-maturing vegetables. Highly tolerant of soil types but need cool weather to grow correctly. Like most veggies, radishes grow quickest in soil that has been worked with organic matter like aged compost or planting mix. Loosen up the soil to a depth of at least 1 foot to allow unhindered growth. Plant at the start of spring. Sow the seeds in rows 6 inches apart. Place seeds close together, roughly 1 inch apart. Thinning usually is not an issue. For a continual harvest, sow seeds weekly until weather begins to warm. You can begin sowing in mid- to late summer as the weather begins to cool for a fall harvest. Radishes are low maintenance. Most important is to water when the soil starts to dry and keep the area weed free. Mulching helps retain water and deter weeds. Harvest as soon as roots are mature. If they sit too long, |

they crack and get tough. Discard any that look diseased or damaged so they do not pass it on to other roots.

Cabbage maggots, flea beetles and carrot fly may affect root growth. If you suspect cabbage maggots, deter them by making floating row covers or make slits in a piece of foam carpet pad or tar paper, securing it around the base of each plant. This prevents maggots from burrowing down to the roots. You know you have flea beetles if they jump in the air like fleas as you bring your hand a few inches over them. To control, take a piece of cardboard or wood and coat one side with a sticky substance. Hover the board a few inches over the radishes and watch the beetles jump up and get stuck. The female carrot fly lays her eggs at the base of root plants. The larvae burrow into the roots. To prevent it, surround the bed with plastic screen.

TIPS ✓

Radish greens have up to 6 times the vitamin C of radishes themselves. Daikons are an Asian white radish grown the same way as red radishes with similar nutrient content and health benefits. Try both to see which you prefer.

Raspberries

**HEALTH
POWER** ＋

Red raspberries are delicious and contain powerful phytonutrients that have antioxidant, antimicrobial and anti-carcinogenic properties. Aside from vitamins C and E, the tannin ellagic acids and a collection of flavonoids are the antioxidants in raspberries, (which outdo kiwis, strawberries and tomatoes). These compounds help protect critical cells and organs from damage caused by free radicals. They also have antimicrobial properties that help suppress certain bacterial colonies (and others like fungi). Research studies suggest some of the phytonutrients in raspberries inhibit initiation of, or halt the growth of, certain cancer cells. Both vitamin K and manganese help build bone matrix and are an excellent source of fiber. Raspberries have a fair amount of sugars, but the fiber and B vitamins slow the absorption of sugars and help break them down faster. Fiber plays a large role in a healthy digestive tract and helps regulate cholesterol levels. Raspberries also provide some folate, which reduces damage in blood vessel walls and supports fetal nerve development.

| VITAMIN & MINERAL |  | Vitamins – C, K, B9 (Folate), E and small amounts of B complex
Minerals – Manganese, Magnesium, Copper, Iron and Potassium |

| DISEASE PREVENTION | | Cardiovascular disease, atherosclerosis, osteoporosis, arthritis, macular degeneration and many cancers (especially colon cancer). |

| HOW TO GROW | | These delectable berries are simple to grow in moderate climates and do really well under organic methods. They take up a lot of room, but produce a plethora of berries. They are self-fertile and require only one variety to fruit. You can usually find healthy, disease resistant cultivars from a local nursery. They grow best in a sunny site in deep, thoroughly worked, moisture-retentive soil. The pH should be 6 or just under. (A pH above 7 causes iron deficiency in raspberries. Bring down the pH well before planting.) Plant in fall to early winter. With bare rooted plants, dig a trench a spade deep and 2 feet wide. Loosen the bottom and amend it with a few inches of well-aged compost, manure or planting mix. Place the canes down into the soil. Amend the soil you dug up as you did on the bottom while filling up the hole. Cut the canes to within 6 inches of the ground to encourage root growth. Separate plants by 3 feet and rows by at least 6 feet. For many varieties, create a post and wire support for the canes to grow along. Embed 6-8 posts in the ground. Connect the posts with wire, one 2 feet above the ground, one in the middle and one on top. As the canes grow, fasten them to the wires as they develop, maintaining a few inches between each cane. In late winter, mulch around the canes with compost or other organic matter. This prevents an iron deficiency. Before the fruit turns red, cover the canes with netting to prevent bird damage. Berries are ripe when the taste is right. To cook with, harvest some just before full ripening. Leave the central core of the fruit on the canes. If you cannot eat them all, store by freezing or canning. For ever-bearing varieties, fruit bears a small crop on the tips of first-year canes each fall and a larger crop on second-year canes. After you harvest all the fruit, cut all the canes that fruited to ground level. Space new canes 3-5 inches apart on the support and remove excess canes. |

| INSECT CONTROL | | Most common pests are birds, aphids and raspberry beetles. Netting deters birds. Planting French marigolds reduces aphids by attracting their predators, ladybugs and hover flies. Raspberry beetle larvae feed on ripe fruit and fall into soil to form pupae. If you see deformed fruit, hoe the |

soil to bring pupae to the surface for birds to eat. If infestation is severe, spray with insecticide like rotenone when the first fruits turn pink.

Yellowing between veins on the leaves shows an iron deficiency. Quickly apply some foliar spray and spread a couple handfuls of nutrient rich fertilizer over the roots.

Rhubarb

HEALTH POWER ✚ Rhubarb is a great source of dietary fiber and helps resolve indigestion issues with its gentle laxative properties. It may also help lower cholesterol and blood pressure. The potassium supports proper nerve functioning and muscle contraction, including the heart. Vitamin C gives rhubarb antioxidant, anti-inflammatory and antiallergenic properties. Vitamin K with calcium adds to bone formation and helps prevent bone breakdown. Rhubarb is low in carbohydrates, saturated fat, sodium and cholesterol. It increases metabolic rate, which is excellent for eating while trying to lose weight. Rhubarb has antibacterial and antifungal properties that may help prevent infections. If applied topically, rhubarb prevents staph infection.

VITAMIN & MINERAL ⬆ Vitamins – K and C
Minerals – Calcium, Potassium, Manganese and Magnesium

DISEASE PREVENTION 🚫 Cholesterol lowering properties support a healthy cardiovascular system free of diseases like atherosclerosis. Vitamin C is an antioxidant that eliminates water-soluble free radicals, many of which may later contribute to cancer. C also protects blood vessels by helping prevent the formation of arterial plaque via its interactions with the bad form of cholesterol (LDL). Vitamin C promotes heart health by stopping potentially fatal plaque-induced clots from causing a heart attack or a stroke. With vitamin K, calcium and manganese, regularly eating rhubarb may help prevent osteoporosis.

HOW TO GROW Rhubarb is an interesting food because it produces fruit, but we eat only the stems. It is an easy, long-lived perennial plant and very cold hardy. Harvest it toward the end of winter through the middle of summer. Prepare the soil by shifting the pH to 7 if not already there. Amend the area with a generous amount of aged compost, manure or highly fertile planting mix. Generally, gardeners do not need more than a few plants. If you want to grow many, plant individuals 2 feet apart in rows 3 feet apart. Depending on time of year, you may find root crowns or potted plants. In spring, or in pots before spring, plant root crowns in soil and cover with a thin layer. Keep the soil moist but never waterlogged. Weed the bed as needed. Let the plants continue to grow through the first year without harvesting. In the second season, harvest the larger stems first as needed, making sure not to take all the stems from one plant. Stems are ripe when they change from green to purplish red. After harvesting each year in the spring, apply another layer of compost or planting mix to promote healthy rejuvenation of reserves once more.

INSECT CONTROL ✗

Common attacking insects include aphids. They are also susceptible to viruses. To deter aphids, companion plant marigolds. They attract both ladybugs and hover flies, which lay their larvae on colonies of aphids for food. They consume thousands this way. Or rinse off the aphids with a strong stream of water that does not damage the host plant. To avoid viruses, get the plant or seeds at a trustworthy nursery. Make sure there is good air circulation and do not waterlog the soil. Keep plants out of low, shady areas. Dispose of infected sections of plants immediately. If all else fails, spray with a copper- or sulfur-based treatment found at nurseries.

TIPS ✓

Enjoy the flowers in the summer time, but do not let the plants run to seed, as this greatly reduces the following harvest. Note: Never eat the leaves of rhubarb, as they contain very harmful toxins, especially if you eat significant amounts.

Rosemary

HEALTH POWER +

Rosemary adds wonderful flavor and aroma to potatoes, pork, lamb and chicken. It also adds helpful substance to a meal by exciting the immune system. It increases circulation (especially to the brain) and improves digestion. It has anti-inflammatory agents that might moderate the severity of asthma attacks or other conditions. The essential oil of rosemary, obtained by steeping in boiling water or steam distillation of all parts of the plant, may help improve memory and support healthy adrenal and lymphatic functions. Some people say its role in aromatherapy is unmatched. Some students use it at exam times to help with memory, mental stimulation and calming the nerves. It has also been noted to relieve headaches, soothe sore muscles, clear out nasal passages and help treat skin conditions like eczema, acne and rashes. Users derive these benefits by adding a bit to topical oils/creams, rubbing a few drops on directly or adding to bath water. A couple of drops have been added to shampoos and conditioners to help condition hair. The oil also has some antiseptic properties and is used to treat respiratory allergies, sore throat and flu.

VITAMIN & MINERAL

Vitamins – traces
Minerals – Iron and Calcium

DISEASE PREVENTION

Given the amount of rosemary included in meals, it is not likely to have a large role in preventing disease. It does add some healthy nutrition to a meal, and the essential oil may prove to be effective in our overall natural health.

HOW TO GROW

Rosemary is an attractive, fuzzy little herb that grows up to 3 feet tall and produces fragrant blue flowers. Great for borders and a generally good plant to have in the garden, as it attracts beneficial insects for pollination and predation. Rosemary does best in a sunny site with soil that has good drainage and plenty of organic matter worked in. It also grows well in containers. Grow them as you like; hedges spaced 1.5 feet apart or individuals 2-3 feet apart. Trim the bushes after flowering, as they will spread along the ground more. If they do, time to replace them. Rosemary is an evergreen. It supplies fresh greens all year round unless temperatures get too cold (as in cold northern climates). To conserve trimmings you cannot eat, dry in a shady, well-ventilated shed. Then put them in airtight jars.

INSECT CONTROL

Virtually no pests threaten rosemary. Use its fragrance to advantage. It repels moths and, in many cases, can attract pollinating insects like bees.

TIPS

Growing rosemary in a container, put pebbles on the bottom for good drainage. Repot container-grown rosemary each year to help the roots spread equally with the plant above ground. Fertilize again each spring.

Rutabaga (Swedes)

HEALTH POWER +

Rutabaga is a great source of vitamin C, folate, fiber, potassium and manganese. See Radishes for the many benefits associated with the antioxidant vitamin C. Folate and vitamin B6 help protect blood vessel walls by converting homocysteine into an inert compound. This keeps homocysteine from reaching high levels where it damages blood vessel walls. Folate is also important for pregnant women to support healthy fetal nerve development. Fiber facilitates smooth digestion and slows down the absorption of sugar and cholesterol, helping to reduce and regulate elevated levels of both. Potassium assists in the proper functioning of muscle and nerve fibers. It can also replace some sodium in the blood and bring down elevated blood pressure. Magnesium is an important cofactor for enzymes involved in detoxification, most notably superoxide dismutase. We need this antioxidant constantly to reduce oxygen free radicals that result from normal respiration in cell mitochondria. If left unchecked, oxygen free radicals can damage cell membranes, mutate DNA and denature proteins. We need magnesium for bone growth and maintenance.

VITAMIN & MINERAL ↑

Vitamins – C, B1 (Thiamin), B6 (Pyridoxine), B9 (Folate) and B3 (Niacin) Minerals – Potassium, Manganese, Magnesium, Phosphorus, Calcium and Iron

DISEASE PREVENTION ⊘

Regularly eating rutabaga may help reduce the symptoms or onset of atherosclerosis, heart disease, osteoporosis, diabetes, constipation, diverticulitis and colorectal cancer.

HOW TO GROW

Swedes, another name for rutabaga, are a member of the cabbage family and one of the easiest veggies to grow. Several varieties to choose from, some of which resist club root and mildew. Choose a resistant cultivar if those problems occur in your area. Swedes also need well-drained soil and a pH above 6.5 to minimize club root. Add lime if necessary. Work some planting mix into soil. Sow the seeds thinly in shallow drills from late spring to early summer. This will help prevent mildew. Space the rows 1 foot apart. Later, thin seedlings to leave the dominant ones 1.5 feet apart. Keep the area weed free. Water when necessary, but do not over water. Mulch overtop with organic matter like aged compost or manure. Harvest after the first frost in fall, remove tops and store in a shady, cool, dry place. Destroy any appearing damaged or diseased.

INSECT CONTROL ✗ Rutabagas are susceptible to flea beetles, which are fun to remove, because they jump when approached. Attach a sticky layer (honey or grease) to one side of a small piece of cardboard and run it a couple inches above the seedlings. Watch the flea beetles jump and get stuck. For other pest problems, consult a trusted local nursery for identification and treatment.

TIPS ✓ They store longer in a container covered lightly with moist peat. If buying in a store, choose heavy, firm rutabagas with smooth, undamaged or un-wrinkled skin.

Sage

HEALTH POWER + The benefits of sage lie in its potent phytonutrients and volatile oils. Cousin to rosemary, sage is another source of rosmarinic acid. The acid is easily absorbed in the intestines and is known for its antioxidant properties. Sage is also a great source of flavonoids and two of the most powerful antioxidants, superoxide dismutase (SOD) and peroxidase. SOD and peroxidase convert strong oxygen free radicals into non-toxic forms. These antioxidant compounds give sage a unique ability to help neutralize toxic forms of oxygen formed during cellular respiration. This in turn prevents oxygen-related damage to cell membranes, vital enzymes and DNA. Some studies suggest sage helps improve cognitive function and memory by preventing the degradation of acetylcholine, a vital neurotransmitter. Sage is also known for antiperspirant, antiseptic, calming and digestive properties. Some commercial antiperspirants contain extracts from sage. Rubbing crushed sage leaves over an open cut or wound can help prevent infection. Regularly eating sage also helps smooth digestion and may help reduce blood sugar levels. In addition to adding sage to your food, you can also prepare a tea with it, which gives a more concentrated dose of the phytonutrients and essential oils.

VITAMIN & MINERAL ↑ Vitamins – traces
Minerals – traces

DISEASE PREVENTION

Regular incorporation of sage in the diet may help reduce the symptoms or the onset of rheumatoid and osteoarthritis, asthma, atherosclerosis, Alzheimer's disease, diabetes and other diseases caused by oxidative damage to cells/organs.

HOW TO GROW

Easy on the eyes and aromatic, sage always serves as a pleasing component of borders. In addition to their colorful, velvety flowers and relaxing aroma, many cultivars add depth to a culinary creation. Sage is a hardy shrub, tolerant of many types of soil pH. Its main site requirements are full sun and good drainage. Amend the soil with plenty of organic matter, especially if it's naturally dense and compacted. Perhaps add some coarse sand to heavier soil. Spring is the time to plant. You can sow from seed, but starting with sage plants in containers or purchasing them bare rooted is easier. Plant both container and bare rooted styles in the ground about 2 feet apart. As they grow, pinch the shoots out to prevent them from getting too lanky. If a couple shoots do get this way, they may be used to layer with (see Tips). Keep the area surrounding them weed free to alleviate nutrient competition. Leaves can be harvested all summer long as needed. Do it before flowering. After that, the flavor is compromised.

INSECT CONTROL

Sage has no common pests that threaten its life.

TIPS

Propagate sage by layering or taking soft wood cuttings. To layer, put an object on top of some of the shoots so they are stuck against the soil. After new roots form, sever the shoot that connects the two plants. You can leave the new plant alone or pot it up and plant it out again in spring. For soft wood cuttings, select a newly grown, healthy shoot about 4-5 inches long. Cut the 4-inch section in half below the leaf joint. Remove the rest of the leaves and plant the end of the cutting in a tray with highly fertile soil. Perhaps dip the cuttings in a fungicide solution and rooting hormone before planting.

Scallions

HEALTH POWER

These young onions have beneficial phytonutrients like flavonoids and sulfur compounds that work together to lower cholesterol, promote heart health, and suppress inflammation. The flavonoid quercetin may bring a number of benefits, including the antioxidant effect in protecting colon cells. Quercetin, along with vitamin C, strengthens the immune system and works against harmful bacteria and viruses that cause common colds or worse. Vitamin C also has antioxidant and anti-inflammatory properties that help deal with arthritis and protect the cardiovascular system from cellular damage and plaque buildup. Vitamin K supports healthy bone development by helping support bone laying components and reducing bone break down by osteoclasts. Also lowers blood pressure. Scallions are a good source of dietary fiber, helping promote healthy digestion and preventing diarrhea. Folate promotes heart health and is critical for healthy fetal nervous system development. Scallions also encourage sweating and urination. In combination with those and the fact that scallions are low in saturated fat, sodium and cholesterol, they are an ideal food to include in a weight loss diet.

VITAMIN & MINERAL

Vitamins – K, C, A and B9 (Folate)
Minerals – Potassium, Iron, Manganese, Calcium, Magnesium, Phosphorus and Copper

DISEASE PREVENTION

Eating vegetables in the Allium family, like garlic, onions, and scallions, may reduce the risk of esophageal, stomach, colon, prostate and possibly breast cancer. Regularly eating reduces pain associated with arthritis and symptoms of asthma.

HOW TO GROW

Scallions (also known as green, spring or salad onions) are a type of onion pulled before they have the chance to develop a full root bulb. The most popular and widely used varieties are perennial versions, Allium fistulosum and Allium cepa. They produce high quality scallions in large quantity. They can be grown from seeds or transplants. Plant seeds thickly about one-half inch deep in well-amended fertile soil. If you want to start during cold winter conditions, sow the seeds indoors until nighttime temperatures rise above freezing. You then need to gradually wean them outdoors when the weather warms up a little. Otherwise, plant the seeds or seedlings outdoors a few weeks before the last frost. Keep rows more than 2 feet apart and slowly thin seedlings out to 6 inches. Once the soil warms up, mulch around and between the plants to deter weeds, retain moisture and buffer the soil so it changes temperatures more slowly. Weed as needed. Be careful not to damage the bulbs. Dry conditions cause bulbs to split. Monitor the moisture level in the soil. Harvest when the shoots are a deep green color and before base begins to swell, usually around mid-summer to fall. The tips should be crisp yet forgiving. You can store in a plastic bag in the refrigerator for about a week. They hold on to their flavor surprisingly well when frozen.

| **INSECT CONTROL** | ✕ | Scallions are generally disease and insect free. They help deter pests like Japanese beetles, carrot flies and aphids from other garden plants. Interplanting is a great way to keep them disease and pest free while helping others. As a preventative, work a good amount of humus into the soil to create good drainage and prevent any potential bacterial or fungal infections. Removing weeds also prevents pests like thrips from persisting over winters. If you have a large, uncontrollable infestation, an insecticidal soap works well in small quantities. |

| **TIPS** | ✓ | Mix in radish plants among the onions to deflect root maggots away from the onions. |

Shallots

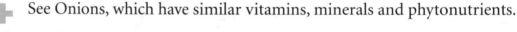

| **HEALTH POWER** | ✚ | See Onions, which have similar vitamins, minerals and phytonutrients. |

| **VITAMIN & MINERAL** | ⬆ | Vitamins – C, B6 (Pyridoxine), B9 (Folate), B1 (Thiamin) and B2 (Riboflavin)
Minerals – Manganese, Potassium, Phosphorus, Magnesium and Calcium |

| **DISEASE PREVENTION** | ⊘ | See Onions |

| **HOW TO GROW** |  | Shallots are a smaller version of the main crop onion with a mild flavor. Harvest them earlier than main crops, too. Shallots need a site with full sunshine and soil full of organic matter. Work in a generous amount of aged compost or planting mix. The pH should be above 6.5; add lime to raise if needed. Shallots are most easily grown from sets (last year's bulbs). Try to choose a variety that stores well for the following year's crop. Remove any dead growth from the top of the bulb and plant in |

drills in spring. Place each bulb 6 inches apart. Barely cover the tip of the bulb with soil. Don't pack the soil down around the bulb, as this will make them pop themselves out when they start to grow roots. They grow best in looser soil that allows for their bulbs to expand and roots to grow without much resistance. Space the rows out by 1 foot and stagger them so sets do not grow right next to each other. Weed as necessary and water during dry weather. Early in summer, loosen the soil around the bulbs to help them ripen up. They are ready for harvest when the foliage dies off. Lift them out, brush the bulbs clean and store. Ideally, put them on a net for optimal airflow, but storing them in perforated sacks in a cool, dry, frost-free place works, too.

INSECT CONTROL ✕ Shallots usually grow trouble free. If you cannot control an infestation by hand, and it threatens the welfare of the crop, consult a local nursery or agricultural extension office.

TIPS ✓ In warmer climates, plant shallots in the fall and take them through winter. Exposure to cool temperatures makes a larger, more flavorful shallot. If your soil is at all dense and drainage is an issue, plant shallots in raised ridges.

Spinach

HEALTH POWER + Spinach is remarkable in the myriad of vitamins, minerals , and phyto-nutrients it gives in one serving. It contains an important carotenoid and a collection of flavonoids that, in addition to vitamins A and C, act as important antioxidants ridding the body of dangerous free radicals. This prevents plaque build up in artery walls by preventing cholesterol from being oxidized. In the end, this helps protect against serious heart problems. Folate and magnesium in spinach also add to heart health by decreasing plaque build up, arterial wall damage (folate) and blood pressure (magnesium and potassium). Because some nutrients are water soluble and others fat soluble, spinach helps resist the growth of various cancerous cells beyond the first day after its consumption. Moreover, nutrients like calcium and Vitamin K add to creating and maintaining healthy bones. The list keeps going with properties that help reduce inflammation in conditions like osteoarthritis, osteoporosis and rheumatoid arthritis. Eating many green leafy vegetables slows down the decline of mental functioning associated with age. Spinach is also an excellent source of iron for helping hemoglobin in blood deliver oxygen to tissues, and lutein that helps maintain eye health. This super food is a great addition to a meal and an ideal way to promote optimal health. Its effects may be profound.

VITAMIN & MINERAL

Vitamins – K, A, C, B9 (Folate), B2 (Riboflavin), B6 (Pyridoxine), E, B1 (Thiamin) and, B3 (Niacin)

Minerals – Manganese, Folate, Magnesium, Iron, Calcium, Potassium, Copper, Phosphorus, Zinc and Selenium

DISEASE PREVENTION

Spinach may help reduce risks in of heart disease, anemia, arthritis, and cancers of the stomach, colon, prostate, breast, ovaries and potentially many more.

HOW TO GROW

Spinach is a garden must. It's packed with great nutrition and easy to grow. Seeds are commonly found in most local nurseries and are more successful than transplants. Plant and harvest spinach in both spring and fall. True spinach is best for cooler climates, but if you want to plant during the summer in a southern, warmer climate, New Zealand spinach copes well with summer heat. If growing in cooler weather, choose a site with lots of sun. In warmer weather, choose a site with plenty of shade. If it gets too warm, spinach will go to seed and reduce yields. The soil needs to be at a pH near 7. Add lime if it's too low. Soil also must be light, fertile and able to hold water well. Adding organic matter in the form of fully aged compost, manure or planting mix works well. Sow each seed in rows roughly half inch deep, spacing seeds a couple inches apart. Space out rows 9-12 inches apart. Spring sowing should begin 6-8 weeks before the last frost. Summer sowing should start in mid-August for cooler climates, later for warmer ones. Thin the sprouts to 6 inches apart to avoid over crowding and premature seeding. Keep the soil moist and free of weeds. Mulching around the plants after they have grown a bit may help retain moisture and deter weeds. The leaves or whole plants should be ready to pick 7-10 weeks after initial sowing.

INSECT CONTROL

Spinach grows in cooler weather and naturally escapes the wrath of many pests. If any, insects that may cause problems are spotted cucumber beetles, leaf miner larvae, aphids, and cabbage loopers. Remove the beetles by hand and dispose of them right away. The larvae of leaf miners embed in the leaves and cause light brown blotches. Remove any leaves showing signs of this infection to stop it from proliferating. This holds true for aphids as well. Remove them or spray with a strong stream of water. Planting French marigolds attracts ladybugs, a natural predator of aphids. If the infestation is too large with beetles, aphids, or loopers, spray with an organic treatment such as insecticidal soap/oil.

TIPS	✓	If you want a continual harvest, try consecutively sowing seeds through spring or early fall. If you're looking to get as much iron from spinach as possible, cooking in iron pans or skillets increases its availability. Make sure to harvest the whole plant at the first hint of bolting to stop the plant from putting all its energy into forming seeds, rendering its the leaves tougher and inedible. Lastly, apply a micronutrient rich fertilizer half way through growth. A planting mix containing soluble seaweed extract or fish bone meal will provide sustenance and steady growth.

Squash (Summer)

HEALTH POWER	+	Summer squash adds similar nutrients as winter squash but in smaller amounts. See Squash (Winter) for health benefits.
VITAMIN & MINERAL	↑	Vitamins – C, A, B9 (Folate), K, B6 (Pyridoxine), B1 (Thiamin), B3 (Niacin) and B2 (Riboflavin) Minerals – Manganese, Magnesium, Potassium, Copper, Phosphorus, Calcium, Zinc and Iron
DISEASE PREVENTION	⊘	See Squash (Winter)
HOW TO GROW	ℯ	Common Summer Squash (zucchini, crookneck and straight neck squash and scallop squash). Thrives in warmer weather. Take about 2 months to ripen. All prefer rich soil in full sun with plenty of organic matter and great drainage. Dig in a generous amount of well-aged compost, manure or planting mix. The pH should be near 6. In mid-spring, sow seeds indoors in 3-inch pots, two seeds to a pot. Sow on a windowsill, under fluorescent light or on a sun porch. Keep soil moist. Thin out seedlings if needed to provide room for the strongest seedling. Plant bush types in

late spring 3 feet apart in rows 5 feet apart. Plant vining cultivars 3 feet apart in rows 8 feet apart. Sow directly outdoors in mid- to late spring when soil temperatures rise to a minimum of 65°F. Create small hills 3 feet apart, with amended soil. Sow seeds 6 per hill. Keep them watered, and thin out to the two best seedlings per hill. Mulch around the seedlings with straw, hay or leaves when the vines are longer and stronger. Fertilize every few weeks, especially after fruits set, with a nutrient-rich fertilizer like compost tea, manure tea or liquid seaweed extract. Summer squash should be nice and plump by late summer. If the ground is always moist at this time, raise them off the ground on bricks or blocks. Harvest summer squash before it matures, and it will continue to set buds. Take care to harvest during a dry time, using a sharp knife you wash between each cut to prevent spreading disease. Cure by letting them dry in the sun until the stems wither. Store in a cool, shaded area.

INSECT CONTROL ✕

Slugs, aphids, vine borers and squash bugs are common pests for squash. Embed a cup of beer in the soil. Slugs and snails are attracted to the cup, crawl in and drown. Plant French marigolds to attract predators of aphids (hover flies and ladybugs) who eat them by the thousands. Or spray aphids off the leaves with a firm stream of water. Avoid this on smaller seedlings. Vine borers are about 1 inch long, look like caterpillars and eat their way into the base of plants leaving behind a sticky sawdust substance. Watch for this sawdust, and cut into stems to remove them or insert Bt (Bacillus thuringiensis) into the stem. Dig dirt up to the stem wound so it can again lay down roots. Watch for the orange and black wasp-like moth in late June when it lays its eggs at the base. They are tiny and reddish orange. If you find them, destroy them and dust or spray with an organic insecticide. Marigolds also help deter squash bugs. They are ¾ inches long and gray brown. They lay their red-brown eggs on the underside of leaves. Handpick them and scan for eggs. Dispose of the pest and eggs when you see them.

TIPS ✓

To avoid disease, water soil not foliage. Keep beds weed free. To ensure fertilization, use a paintbrush to transfer pollen from the male stamen to the female pistil.

Squash (Winter) -

HEALTH POWER

Research is limited, though some phytonutrients found in winter squash have been linked with anti-cancer properties in studies of other plants. Winter squash is a good source of all the vitamins and minerals listed. More nutrient-dense than its cousin, the summer squash. Most notable in one serving of winter squash are vitamins A (more than 100 percent RDA) and C (more than 30 percent RDA). These vitamins team up for many functions. They support the immune response of white blood cells toward pathogens. They act as antioxidants in water soluble areas of the body, protecting cells from free radical damage. Some major antioxidant actions help prevent the buildup of plaque in blood vessels, reduce inflammation and help prevent damage to cells in the eye. Winter squash gives potassium, key to maintaining normal blood pressure, nerve cell transmission and muscle contraction. High fiber content supports digestion, removes excess cholesterol and helps regulate blood sugar. Pregnant women need the B vitamin folate for normal fetal neural development. Also contributes to heart health by preventing homocysteine, an amino acid that in high concentrations causes blood vessel stiffening. With other B vitamins, squash helps make energy through the metabolism of lipids, carbohydrates and proteins.

VITAMIN & MINERAL

Vitamins – A, C, B9 (Folate), B1 (Thiamin), B6 (Pyridoxine), B3 (Niacin) and B5 (Pantothenic acid)
Minerals – Potassium, Manganese, Copper, Iron and Magnesium

DISEASE PREVENTION

May reduce risk and symptoms of benign prostate hypertrophy (BPH), atherosclerosis, diabetic heart disease, heart attack, stroke, colon cancer (potentially others), asthma, osteoarthritis and rheumatoid arthritis.

HOW TO GROW

Common Winter Squash (butternut, acorn, delicious Hubbard, banana, buttercup and spaghetti squash). Thrives in warmer weather. Winter vining cultivars may grow 10-20 feet long and require generous space. Winter squash takes 3-4 months to mature. Prefers rich soil in full sun with plenty of organic matter and great drainage. Dig in a generous amount of well-aged compost, manure or planting mix. The pH should be near 6. In mid-spring, sow seeds indoors in 3-inch pots, two seeds to a pot. Sow on a windowsill, under fluorescent light or on a sun porch. Keep soil moist.

Thin out seedlings if needed to provide room for the strongest seedling. Plant bush types in late spring 3 feet apart in rows 5 feet apart. Plant vining cultivars 3 feet apart in rows 8 feet apart. Sow directly outdoors in mid to late spring when soil temperatures rise to a minimum of 65°F. Create small hills 6 feet apart with amended soil. Sow seeds 6 per hill. Keep them watered, and thin out to the two best seedlings per hill. Mulch around the seedlings with straw, hay or leaves when the vines are longer and stronger. Fertilize every few weeks, especially after fruits set, with a nutrient-rich fertilizer like compost tea, manure tea or liquid seaweed extract. If the ground is always moist at this time, raise them off the ground on bricks or blocks. Harvest only when it is fully mature, as the taste depends on it. Do this just before the first expected frost, and they will store longer. Harvest during a dry time, using a sharp knife you wash between each cut to prevent spreading disease. Cure by letting dry in the sun until the stems wither. Store in a cool, shaded area to extend storage time.

| INSECT CONTROL | ✕ | See Squash (Summer) for common pests and their control methods. |

| TIPS | ✓ | To avoid disease, water soil not foliage. Keep beds weed free. To ensure fertilization, use a paintbrush to transfer pollen from the male stamen to the female pistil. |

Strawberries

| HEALTH POWER | + | Loaded with Vitamin C. (A single berry can have up to 20 percent of the RDA.) This antioxidant combined with ellagic acid and anthocyanin helps heal wounds faster, strengthens the immune system and helps delay age-related memory loss. The folate in one serving helps reduce neural tube birth defects and damage to arteries. The fiber helps prevent constipation. |

| VITAMIN & MINERAL | ⬆ | Vitamins – C, Folate, B2 (Riboflavin), B5 (Pantothenic Acid), B6 (Pyridoxine) & K
Minerals – Manganese, Iodine, Potassium, Magnesium and Copper |

DISEASE PREVENTION ⊘ Strawberries are anti-inflammatory, helping prevent rheumatoid and osteoarthritis and asthma. The diverse content of minerals and phytonutrients in strawberries may also greatly reduce the risk of atherosclerosis, heart disease, macular degeneration and many cancers. Acts like aspirin and ibuprofen but without the negative side effects.

HOW TO GROW A great addition to the garden. Easy on the eyes and taste buds with great health benefits. Four different types of strawberries bear fruit at different times: June bearers, Ever-bearers, Day-Neutrals and Alpine. June bearers yield all fruit within a month, depending on climate variation. Ever-bearers offer a good amount at the beginning of summer, scattered in the middle and a small spread in late summer. Day-Neutrals bear fruit throughout the season between frostings. They are sensitive to extremes and require babysitting. Buy at your local nursery, but ensure they are certified disease-free. Strawberries do well in both pots and garden rows. They like a soil pH just below neutral (7). They also need good drainage and moisture-retentive soil. Pick a site with plenty of sun and good airflow. If drainage is poor, you can increase it by tilling and raising your bed. Work in a couple handfuls of planting mix per square yard or a few inches of compost. Plant them 2 feet apart in rows separated by 1.5 feet. You can also lay down polypropylene and plant them in slits. This warms the soil and protects from weeds, but is not a requirement. Dig holes deep enough that the soil will come up to where the leaves begin on the shoots. In the bottom of the hole, form a small cone and set the plant over it, arranging the roots around it. Fill in with the amended soil. If you trim back most of the runners sent out during the growing season, the plant will dedicate more energy to growing large fruits. Water them thoroughly with about one inch of water a week (more in warmer climates). Avoid water logging, as strawberries can mildew. Harvest berries when they are a nice red. Freeze if necessary.

INSECT CONTROL ✕ Pests include birds, slugs, snails, aphids and red spider mite. Stop slugs and snails with a beer trap implanted in soil. A scarecrow might work for some birds but not many. Only row covers effectively stop birds. Stop aphids by planting marigolds to attract their predators (ladybugs and hover flies). Spider mites, most active on dry days, cause leaves to mottle yellow and fall off. Spray regularly with water. If the attack is bad, use rotenone as a last resort.

TIPS ✓ Weeding is a must to produce healthy strawberries. Lay down a layer of straw mulch around plants during growing season to separate the strawberries from soil and help keep them weed free. Harvest ripe berries as soon as they are ready. Immediately discard any that are malformed or mildewing. Rotate crops every three seasons to maintain healthy soil and good yields. Create new plants for the next season by collecting runners in pots. Choose disease-resistant cultivars adapted to your temperatures and day length. To avoid mildew and viruses, do not over water, and keep air circulating well.

Sunflower

HEALTH POWER + Providing nearly 100 percent of the vitamin E RDA in ¼ cup, sunflower seeds are an excellent source of the main fat-soluble antioxidant. It helps reduce oxidative damage that can cause plaque build up in the arteries, thickening of arteries and joint inflammation. Of the nuts and seeds, sunflower seeds have one of the highest concentrations of phytosterols, phytonutrients with similar structures to cholesterol and linked to lowering their levels in the blood. Some research evidence shows if we eat a moderate amount of these cholesterol substitutes, they have high potential to reduce the damaging effects of cholesterol. Sunflower seeds are a concentrated source of the intermediary mineral magnesium, which is important for biochemical processes in energy production, the synthesis of essential compounds (proteins, enzymes, DNA, lipids, the antioxidant glutathione), cellular communication (proper muscle, nerve function) and bone matrix formation. A deficiency in magnesium may contribute to higher blood pressure, migraine headaches, muscle spasms/cramps, soreness and fatigue. Selenium is a trace mineral in these seeds that is a cofactor/activator for many enzymes and proteins that help the body maintain healthy DNA, prevent proliferation of cancer cells (by inhibiting growth and inducing apoptosis), and helping detoxify the body by marking dangerous compounds for destruction.

VITAMIN & MINERAL ↑ Vitamins – E, B1 (Thiamin), B5 (Pantothenic Acid) and B9 (Folate)
Minerals – Manganese, Magnesium, Copper, Tryptophan, Selenium and Phosphorus

DISEASE PREVENTION Regularly eating unsalted sunflower seeds may reduce the symptoms or onset of asthma, hypertension, rheumatoid and osteoarthritis, osteoporosis, hot flashes, diabetes, atherosclerosis, cardiovascular disease and many cancers.

HOW TO GROW A great way to brighten up both the garden and daily nutrition. Grow sunflower for its visual appeal and its seeds, sprouts and greens. All are highly nutritious. Sunflowers are easy to grow and tolerant of soil types. Choose a sunny site next to vegetables or in the flower garden where they will not shade other plants needing sun. For optimum growth and a beautiful flower, work in some compost or planting mix to increase soil fertility. The time to plant is spring after the last frost. Sow seeds directly into the bed where they will grow. Place them ½ inch deep and 1 foot apart. They sprout soon afterward as the seeds germinate in roughly 3-5 days. Water regularly when they are young and keep the bed weed free. After they reach 1 foot tall, mulch around the base to help retain moisture and deter weeds. The heads grow to the size of a dinner plate in some cultivars. Keep the soil moist during flowering to promote productivity. They are ready to harvest when they dip over. Cut them 2 feet below the flower and hang upside down in a dry, sheltered area for a few days with a cloth underneath to catch any seeds that fall. Then rub off the seeds and store for any occasion.

INSECT CONTROL Sunflowers are generally pest free and attract beneficial insects to the garden that can help control other pests. Protect the seeds from birds by covering the flowers with mesh, pantyhose or hole-punched plastic bags.

TIPS Save a couple heads with their stalks to hang up to use as bird feeders. This may help keep the birds from other plants in the garden and provide them with good sustenance.

Sweet Potatoes

HEALTH POWER A great source of vitamin A (in the form of beta-carotene) and vitamin C. Sweet potatoes have antioxidant properties that help remove damaging free radicals that affect the cardiovascular system, eyes and digestive tract. They also slow the biochemical reactions that cause inflammation, which helps with a number of painful conditions. Vitamin B6 reduces homocysteine levels in the blood. (High homocysteine levels are correlated with increased vascular and heart conditions.) B6 also supports nervous system function by helping nerve cells communicate and helping to synthesize neurotransmitters. Vitamin B6 helps relieve bloating and acne during premenstrual stress. Potassium good for maintaining normal blood pressure. Fiber and B vitamins promote smooth digestion and efficient metabolism of nutrients from food.

VITAMIN & MINERAL

Vitamins – A, C, B6 (Pyridoxine), B5 (Pantothenic Acid), B3 (Niacin), B1 (Thiamin) and B2 (Riboflavin)
Minerals – Manganese, Potassium, Copper, Magnesium, Phosphorus and Iron

DISEASE PREVENTION

The antioxidants in sweet potatoes help treat or prevent atherosclerosis, colon cancer and diabetic heart disease. Their anti-inflammatory properties help reduce the severity of arthritis and asthma. The vitamin B6 in sweet potatoes helps defend against heart attack and stroke. High levels of vitamins A and C help protect eyes against cataracts and macular degeneration. Vitamin A deficiency is linked with cigarette smoke, raising the risk of emphysema for those exposed to it. Vitamin A in sweet potatoes can help counter the effects of inhaling smoke.

HOW TO GROW

These tubers grow only in warm, sunny climates. Sweet potatoes prefer loose, sandier soil, but will grow in heavier soils if amended with plenty of organic matter for good drainage. Work in a bit of compost or planting mix to create raised ridges or beds about 8 inches high. Buy plants from a nursery. Plant a few weeks after the last frost in rows or beds, spacing plants 1.5 feet apart in rows 3.5 feet apart. You can also plant single plants in hills 3 feet apart. Water regularly after planting, but reduce watering near the end of growing season (end of summer) so potatoes do not crack. During growing season, gently lift vines and shift them around so they do not lay down roots in unplanned spots. Keep the area weed free. In a cold climate, cover the rows with black polythene and plant through slits cut into the plastic. They mature and are ready to harvest when vines turn yellow. Keep them in the ground to extend the growing season until the first frost. After that, the vines turn black. Carefully dig them up from underneath the side of the row by cutting the foliage. Cure by letting them dry out in the sun before storing. Use any damaged ones as soon as possible.

INSECT CONTROL ✕ Wireworms, aphids, slugs and cutworms can hurt sweet potatoes. Wireworms make small holes in potatoes that look like slug damage. If the soil is newly used, grow a line of wheat between rows to attract the wireworms. Dig up and dispose of the wheat. Cutworms feed on the base of the plant during the day and can destroy it. If plants fall over, look just beneath the soil to see if they are the cause. If so, dig up the soil around the plants and dispose of any cutworms you see. Growing ground cover will attract ground beetles that will eat the worms. To stop slugs, sink a cup of beer into the soil. The slugs crawl in and drown. For aphids, grow marigold trees to attract their predators. Also spray them off the plants with a strong water stream.

TIPS ✓ You can harvest the potatoes in mid-summer before they reach full potential. They taste roughly the same but are a little smaller. Regularly check through the stored tubers and remove any showing signs of rot.

Swiss Chard

HEALTH POWER ✚ Chard is off the high end of the chart with its vitamin and mineral content. One cup gives 700 percent of the RDA of vitamin K, more than 100 percent of vitamin A and 50 percent of vitamin C. It is also an excellent source of magnesium, potassium, iron, fiber and more. The health potential of chard seems endless. The vitamin K, magnesium and calcium in chard give a great boost for more bone building and less bone loss. Vitamin A supports healthy vision, immune system function, lung health and protects thin membrane layers around organs and blood vessels. Minerals in chard can also help keep normal blood pressure while vitamins A, C and E do the same by preventing the build up of plaque and the blockage of blood flow in arteries. Magnesium and potassium are the main minerals that help with blood pressure and heart function by supporting muscle and nerve function. Iron is needed to deliver oxygen to tissues all over the body. Eating chard regularly also has the potential to lower high levels of cholesterol and blood sugar, mainly from its fiber content. Chard also helps the body activate crucial antioxidant molecules from the liver to help get rid of potentially dangerous metabolic wastes. Studies also suggest regular eating of vegetables like chard can slow down age-related cognitive decline. The long list of benefits shows chard is a flat out supporter of overall health.

VITAMIN & MINERAL

Vitamins – K, A, C, E, B2 (Riboflavin), B6 (Pyridoxine), B1 (Thiamin), B9 (Folate), B3 (Niacin) and B5 (Pantothenic Acid)
Minerals – Magnesium, Manganese, Potassium, Iron, Copper, Calcium, Phosphorus and Zinc

DISEASE PREVENTION

Regularly eating chard may reduce the symptoms or the onset of osteoporosis, asthma, rheumatoid and osteoarthritis, anemia, hypertension, cardiovascular disease, diabetes, lung cancer, colon cancer and potentially many other cancers due to its antioxidants and detoxifiers, vitamins and minerals.

HOW TO GROW

Relatively easy to grow, Swiss chard is loaded with nutrition and seen as a delicacy in some parts of the world. You can grow two distinctly colored varieties: red and white stemmed. Although red stem is more attractive, it has no better flavor than the other. Chard needs highly fertile soil that retains moisture yet drains well. Work some organic matter into the site, like compost or planting mix, to create a nice loamy soil. The pH must be above 6.5; add lime if needed. Plant chard in mid-spring. In warmer climates, a late summer or early fall sowing works, too. Sow seeds in groups of 3 in shallow drills spacing each cluster out by 1 foot and each row by roughly 1.5 feet. Later thin out to leave the strongest seedling per cluster. Once the seedlings emerge, keep the soil moist and the bed weed free. Harvesting can begin in mid-summer. Pull, do not cut, leaves off the plant. (Cutting makes them bleed.) It is a "cut and come again" plant. Harvest from around the outside of the plant as you need and they grow right back. They are cold hardy enough to handle light frosts, so you can harvest into the fall/winter.

INSECT CONTROL

Slugs, caterpillars, cucumber beetles and mealy cabbage aphids may try snacking on chard. Slugs can be controlled by embedding a wide cup of beer in the soil. Slugs are attracted to it, slide in and drown. You can also remove by hand and destroy mornings and evenings. Remove caterpillars by hand, too. Watch for their eggs on the leaves and wipe them off. If infestation is uncontrollable, spray with Bt. Cucumber beetles can be removed by hand, too, but if they are too resilient, spray with rotenone. Cabbage aphids cluster on the underside of leaves. Control them by companion planting French marigolds or another smaller flowering plant. They will attract hoverflies and ladybugs that consume aphids by the score.

TIPS ✓ Chard germinates easily. You might enjoy starting from scratch by sowing seeds directly into an outdoor planting bed. This also gives you more choice among varieties. Sow seeds in early spring, and find a recipe that works for you.

Tarragon

HEALTH POWER + You can gain the many health benefits of tarragon by using teas, dried/fresh leaves, the essential oil and tinctures. (Tarragon mixed with isopropyl alcohol makes a good disinfectant.) Tarragon contains caffeic acid, which can stop or kill many bacteria, viruses and fungi. It makes a good cleansing disinfectant to rub on wounds or can be used as a deodorant. Components of tarragon help digestion by stimulating the secretion of digestive compounds in the saliva as well as gastric fluids (like bile and other acids) into the lower digestive tract. This stimulates faster processing of foods already in the stomach (which helps get rid of wastes and potential toxins faster) and increases appetite. Its antimicrobial action enables tarragon to kill intestinal worms. Tarragon also increases circulation, which helps distribute nutrients, oxygen, hormones and enzymes to tissues and remove toxins. Tarragon has calming properties, too. Many people use it to help relax the nerves and facilitate a good night's sleep. Despite these health benefits, use in moderation. Tarragon oil contains estragole, which is toxic at high levels. As an extra precaution, young children and pregnant women should avoid the oil. The spice is safe, as the essential oil concentrations are too small to cause harm.

VITAMIN & MINERAL Vitamins – B6 (Pyridoxine), A, C and B2 (Riboflavin)
Minerals – Manganese, Iron, Calcium, Magnesium and Potassium

DISEASE PREVENTION Plays a role in helping reduce the symptoms or delaying the onset of rheumatism, indigestion, anorexia, insomnia and excessive flatulence.

HOW TO GROW Tarragon is a hardy perennial herb tolerant of many soil types. It comes in two varieties, French and Russian. The French has a far superior flavor for cooking purposes. Tarragon plants prefer a sheltered site with full sun and good drainage. The best way to grow is from purchased young plants. Growing French tarragon from seed is not an option, but the Russian variety sows easily. Plant them 1.5 feet apart. Water regularly as necessary to keep the soil moist. Weed also to prevent nutrient competition. Harvest the leaves throughout the season. You can store them in vinegar or dry them. If you choose vinegar, wash it off before eating, and then use the vinegar in a salad dressing. For French tarragon, put a few inches of mulch over the top to protect from direct contact with frost. They need to be lifted, divided and replanted every 3-4 years to maintain tastiness in the leaves. They should grow well enough to divide into many plants every spring. To divide them, manually lift them out and divide in half by hand or use a back-to-back garden shovel/fork. Once out, cut all the leaves down to about 2 inches from the roots and replant right away.

INSECT CONTROL Tarragon is generally pest free.

TIPS For a good sleepy time tea, try it mixed with chamomile just before bedtime.

Thyme

HEALTH POWER Thyme is a healthy source of vitamin K, giving more than 60 percent of RDA in two teaspoons. It also contains iron, manganese, calcium and dietary fiber. It is an old-time remedy for chest and respiratory illness. The benefits come from the essential oils and flavonoids, which have antioxidant, antifungal and antibacterial functions. The oil thymol has antioxidant powers that help increase the good fats in cells and their membranes. It also works as an antibacterial agent against Salmonella, E. coli, Shigella and others. You can create your own surface cleaning/disinfectant spray by mixing thyme, boiling water and a little liquid soap in a spray bottle.

VITAMIN & MINERAL

Vitamins – K
Minerals – Iron, Magnesium and Calcium

DISEASE PREVENTION

Thymol oil helps fight inflammatory diseases by stopping an enzyme, elastase, from breaking down elastin, which, with collagen, affects the mechanical abilities of connective tissue, especially in the throat and lungs. Thyme also contains a collection of terpenoids, which are thought to reduce or prevent cancer tissue formation. Regularly eating thyme supports bone health and may help prevent osteoporosis and anemia.

HOW TO GROW

Thyme is more than a nice aesthetic addition to your garden. It also attracts many pollinating insects for flowers and serves as a nutritious spice. Thyme needs a sunny spot with good drainage. Ideal pH for nutrient uptake is near 7. Add lime to raise, if needed. Two popular types of thyme are used for cooking, common and lemon thyme. Sow common thyme from seed outdoors after the last frost in spring or, more commonly, buy in containers and transplant any time. They spread a lot, so plant at least a foot apart, depending on how soon you want to establish ground cover. Thyme is tolerant of poor-quality soil. A few handfuls of planting mix will ensure nice growth. Pinch the growth tips frequently to encourage shorter, denser growth. Trim back after they flower, too, and the plant will continue to produce. You can continue to pick the leaves as you want for a fresh herb to add to a variety of dishes.

INSECT CONTROL

Thyme is pest free. Many insects avoid thyme, and planting it can be a great natural deterrent. Some common garden bugs, spider mites or aphids may be a problem. Spray with an insecticidal soap. You can also plant dandelions or marigolds nearby to attract ladybugs, a natural predator of aphids and mites.

TIPS

The leaves have more flavor dry than fresh. Dry them in a well-ventilated area before using. Thyme is a great aromatic addition to the garden. Some types can be used as a flowering ground cover. If you live in the North, you may need to protectively cover the plants with something like large evergreen branches.

Tomato

A great supporter of overall health. Tomatoes have a lot of vitamins C and A, plus beta-carotene and the pigment lycopene, all super antioxidants that help prevent cell damage by free radical oxygen molecules. These phytonutrients work in synergy with other vitamins and minerals in tomatoes to promote heart and bone health and protect against inflammation and a number of cancers. (The cardiovascular benefits come from helping to regulate blood pressure and reduce damage to blood vessels from oxidative stress, plaque buildup and elevated homocysteine levels.) Regularly eating tomatoes can lower cholesterol levels, promote proper fetal development and regulate blood sugar. The B vitamins help make use of the energy in food.

Vitamins – C, A, K, B1 (Thiamin), B6 (Pyridoxine), B9 (Folate), B3 (Niacin), B2 (Riboflavin), B5 (Pantothenic Acid) and E
Minerals – Molybdenum, Potassium, Manganese, Chromium, Copper, Magnesium, Iron and Phosphorus

Tomatoes reduce the risk of cardiovascular disease, rheumatoid and osteoarthritis and asthma. They also help prevent cataracts and lower the risk of prostate, breast, lung, stomach, pancreatic, colon, rectal and endometrial cancers.

Plant in full sun, amend the soil well with a good compost or planting mix. They prefer a pH of 6. Tomatoes grow and produce best outdoors. They can also grow in containers (minimum 15 gallons of potting soil) but not to their full potential. More soil volume is best. Start from seed indoors 6 weeks before the last frost, or buy transplants from a local nursery. Plant seedlings or transplants in space at least 2 feet square. Keep the fruit from drooping onto the ground by growing the upright varieties against canes or wire cages. Pinch out the tops after they make 3-4 groups of fruits. For bush varieties, cover the soil underneath the plants (using bark or similar) so fruits develop off the ground. They are heavy feeders and can take copious amounts of fertilizer. Keep plants moist but not sopping wet to avoid fungal diseases.

INSECT CONTROL ✗ Tomatoes are susceptible to tomato hornworm. Spray foliage with Bt (Bacillus thuringiensis) for natural control. You can also remove worms by hand early in the morning. Worms are usually on top of the foliage and are easy to remove and discard. As a general measure, you can spray with a botanical insecticide-fungicide for natural control of most insect pests and diseases, such as early blight, gray leaf spot, late blight, Septoria leaf spot, Southern blight and verticillium wilt.

TIPS ✓ Pick or buy tomatoes fully ripe, the redder the better. Ripe tomatoes may have 4 times more beta-carotene than green, immature ones. This makes backyard tomatoes the best. You know they were not picked green and shipped to ripen weeks later.

Turnips

HEALTH POWER ✚ Turnip roots are high in Vitamin C. With the greens, their high content of vitamins, minerals and phytonutrients are a great promoter of overall health. Turnips and turnip greens help create more bone mass by slowing osteoclastic (break down) processes and increasing osteoblastic (building) processes. Turnips and their greens are loaded with vitamins A, C and E, which reinforce immune system, maintain healthy membranes and connective tissue (for example, blood vessels and joints), protect important cells (eyes and vascular system) from free radical damage and reduce inflammation. Turnips also give dietary fiber that helps maintain healthy digestion and regulates cholesterol levels. Along with the free radical fighters, fiber promotes overall health and efficient functioning of the colon. Turnips and their greens also support heart health. The antioxidants (vitamins C, A and E) directly protect the structure and function of blood vessels and minimize the buildup of plaque on vessel walls. Vitamins B6 and folate also prevent damage to vessel walls by minimizing the potentially harmful chemical homocysteine. This vegetable also supports healthy metabolism, lung health and brain function.

VITAMIN & MINERAL ⬆ (Roots and Greens):
Vitamins – K, A, C, B9 (Folate), B6 (Pyridoxine), E, B2 (Riboflavin), B1 (Thiamin), B5 (Pantothenic Acid) and B3 (Niacin)

Minerals – Manganese, Calcium, Copper, Potassium, Magnesium, Iron and Phosphorus

DISEASE PREVENTION

Helps reduce symptoms or onset of osteoporosis, macular degeneration, cardiovascular disease, rheumatoid and osteoarthritis, anemia, diabetes, female liver cancer and cancers of the prostate, stomach, colon, lung, pancreas and bladder.

HOW TO GROW

One of the easier root veggies to grow. You can sow turnips indoors in early winter or outdoors in mid-spring to mid-summer. Turnips prefer well-amended, fertile soil with good drainage and a pH above 6.5. If sowing indoors, you can multi-sow them by planting six seeds per tray cell or pocket made in the container. Cover seeds with a small layer of soil and/ or sand. Place them in a greenhouse or under a fluorescent light in an area where the temperature is mid-60's or higher. Plant the seedlings 12 inches apart under a covering (cloche) in early spring. If sowing outdoors, create shallow drills about a foot apart and plant seeds along each drill. Cover them with a thin layer of soil and keep them well watered. After seedlings reach a couple inches tall, thin them out to 6-8 inches apart in their rows. Especially during the early stages, keep the plots weed free by hand pulling or hoeing. Mulching between the plants with some well-aged compost or other organic matter provides insulation, retains moisture, deters weeds and may give some sustenance. Harvest the first turnips when they are the size of ping pong balls. Harvest the others no larger than baseball size. For outdoor crops, they are plump and ready near mid-fall. Twist off shoots on top and store unused ones in moist sand or peat at moderate temperatures.

INSECT CONTROL

Turnips are rather pest free. Flea beetles bother them. These little creatures eat small holes in the leaves of seedlings, which can delay harvest or even kill them. As with fleas, they leap in the air when something gets close. Use this defense against them by using a small, flat piece of wood or plastic with a sticky layer of honey or grease on it. Run the piece of wood an inch above the beetles, and watch them jump up and get stuck.

TIPS

Turnips grow best in temperatures of 50-75°F. (Any higher and the roots get woody and bitter.) Before harvesting, loosen up the soil first with a garden fork. The smaller roots are the most tender; pull them up before they get too big. Discard damaged roots, as they may spread infection to the undamaged roots in storage.

Walnuts

HEALTH POWER +

They lack many common vitamins and minerals, but walnuts have profound phytonutrients for your health. They are a great source of omega-3 fatty acids, an essential fat the body cannot make. Omega-3's in walnuts help protect the heart, have anti-inflammatory properties, encourage healthy brain function and help prevent many cancers. An omega-3 found in walnuts is also linked to healthy bones. Walnuts are high in fats, but these are good fats linked to lowering the risk of weight gain. They also have monounsaturated fats, which reduce the bad form of cholesterol (LDL) and the threat of clotting in arteries. Walnuts also have arginine, an essential amino acid the body cannot produce. This amino acid helps maintain smooth and elastic blood vessel walls by helping produce nitric oxide, which relaxes the smooth muscle around blood vessels. Walnuts also have many antioxidants that keep free radicals from damaging cells, especially in the cardiovascular system. Eating walnuts regularly is linked to a decrease in blood pressure. Walnuts can actually undo some of the damaging biochemical reactions caused by eating foods high in saturated fats. Cell membranes are made of fats. Introducing flexible omega-3 fatty acids increases a cell membrane's flexibility and ability to communicate and excrete wastes. This is especially important in the brain, helping us grow closer to our full cognitive potential. Walnuts give melatonin, an antioxidant that also supports healthy biorhythms. Together all these factors make walnuts a heart-smart choice.

VITAMIN & MINERAL ↑

Vitamins – B6 (Pyridoxine), B9 (Folate), B1 (Thiamin), B2 (Riboflavin) and B5 (Pantothenic Acid)
Minerals – Manganese, Copper, Magnesium, Phosphorus, Zinc, Iron, and Potassium

DISEASE PREVENTION ⊘

A power house in preventing heart disease, atherosclerosis, high blood pressure, heart attack, stroke and gallstones. Research suggests antioxidants in walnuts, such as ellagic acid, reduce the risk of many forms of cancer.

HOW TO GROW

Two types of walnut trees grow, the black walnut and the Persian/English walnut. The black walnut tree grows from 50-100 feet tall. The English walnut tree grows smaller, about 40-60 feet. Both make big-spread shade trees. These trees need full sun, great drainage and a deep, highly fertile soil. Nuts are ready to harvest in the fall. Plant a seedling from a reputable nursery instead of trying to plant seeds into the ground yourself. Squirrels usually find the nut and devour it. Be sure to dig the hole deep enough for the taproot to comfortably fit in. Mulch around the trunk with a thick layer of compost or other material, but leave a space between the trunk and the mulch to keep rodents from injuring it. Water the tree thoroughly once a week, especially in dry weather when it is young. English walnuts are popularly grown for nut production, especially in California. Most cultivars are self-fertile but will give more nuts with other walnut trees nearby. Nuts are ready to harvest in the fall 3-7 years after planting the tree. You need prune only dead or diseased branches on this tree if using it for food.

INSECT CONTROL

Some pests can infiltrate a walnut tree, but none are a large threat to a healthy tree growing in healthy soil. If leaf grubbing caterpillars become a problem, Bt (Bacillus thurigiensis) takes care of them. Pick up fallen sticks, husks and leaves so pests do not have a home or food over the winter.

TIPS

Check with your local nursery before buying a walnut seedling, as the tree's roots excrete the chemical juglone and may be toxic for other plants nearby. Place the walnut tree far enough from other plants that its roots cannot reach them (usually 1.5 times the height of the tree).

Watercress

HEALTH POWER

An excellent source of vitamin K and a good source of calcium, watercress helps maintain strong bones and healthy blood clotting. It also donates about half the RDA of both antioxidant vitamins A (also in the form of beta carotene) and C. These are key factors in protecting cells and organs from oxidative damage by free radicals. They also help support a healthy immune response, eyesight, skin and cardiovascular system (by preventing plaque build up and maintaining elasticity in blood vessel walls). Watercress also has small amounts of vitamins B1, B6, E and the minerals magnesium, iron, iodine and zinc. These support the thyroid gland, stimulate metabolism, synthesize red blood cells and stimulate the production of antibodies to fight infections. Watercress has the phytonutrients lutein and zeaxanthin, which work alongside beta-carotene and vitamin A to maintain healthy eyesight. The glucosinolates help boost and regulate the liver's production of detoxification enzymes. The phenylethyl isothiocyanates in watercress are being studied for their potential to fight the development of cancer cells.

VITAMIN & MINERAL

Vitamins – K, C and A
Minerals – Calcium, Manganese and Potassium

DISEASE PREVENTION

Regularly eating watercress may help reduce the risk of cardiovascular disease, heart attack, stroke, cataracts, gout, osteoporosis, lung cancer, breast cancer and potentially many other cancers.

HOW TO GROW

Watercress is a great addition to soups, salads, sandwiches, dips and sauces. It grows naturally in running rivers and streams, but is also easy to cultivate in the backyard. It prefers to grow in shade with excellent water retention. Dig a trench about 1 foot deep. Layer the bottom with some aged compost/manure or planting mix. Work in some organic matter with the soil dug out and fill the trench. In early spring, sow seeds at temperature close to 55°F. If sowing indoors, use seed trays. When the seedlings get big enough, transfer them to another tray with wider spacing using a mini dibber and holding onto the leaves only. Do not touch the stems during the transfer. Plant them out in late spring to early summer spacing them out by about 4 inches. If your climate is warm enough, sow seeds outside in shallow drills. Once they grow a bit, remove the weaker ones and leave a spacing of about 4 inches. Another way is to buy a bundle of watercress, take the shoots with a couple young roots showing and plant them in the same spacing. Water generously and often. Keep the bed weed free by handpicking and/or hoeing. No other fertilizing is needed. Pinch the dominant shoots and remove any flowers as soon as you see them. Harvest the shoots as needed. They come back for another harvest until temperatures drop in fall.

✕ Watercress is largely pest free. If something you do not recognize begins to infest, take one of the pests to the nearest nursery and/or agricultural extension office for an ID and advice on the best treatment.

✓ Watercress can be grown indoors in pots with drainage holes. Place pots on an open tray of water. Refill the tray as soil soaks up water. Keep the soil damp. Prevent flowering by pruning buds immediately. Greens wither and wilt quickly. Use right after harvesting.

Watermelon

+ Watermelon packs a punch with important vitamins and phytonutrients. The combination of antioxidant vitamins C and A does wonders for the body. They both stop free radicals from causing damage to cells that otherwise lead to many ailments: plaque build up in arteries through the oxidation of cholesterol, increased inflammation, especially in joints, vision deterioration and cellular damage that can lead to mutations in DNA (which can become cancerous). Watermelon is also a great source of the phytonutrient lycopene, which has received much attention for its antioxidant behavior and ability to reduce the risk of many cancers. Watermelon is also a great fruit source of B vitamins, which the body uses to generate energy from sugars, carbohydrates, lipids (fats), amino acids and proteins. Another phytonutrient, citrulline (an amino acid, too) gets converted to the amino acid arginine. Higher levels of arginine are linked to relaxing blood vessels (through increased production of nitric oxide) removing the waste product ammonia and increasing cell sensitivity to the insulin molecule.

↑ Vitamins – C, A, B6 (Pyridoxine) and B1 (Thiamin)
Minerals – Potassium and Magnesium

⊘ Watermelon may help reduce the symptoms or prevent the onset of rheumatoid/osteoarthritis, colon cancer, asthma, heart disease, type II diabetes, erectile dysfunction, and cancers of the lung, breast, prostate, colon, rectum and endometrium.

HOW TO GROW

Watermelon has the same environmental and cultivation needs as other melons (cantaloupe and honeydews) but falls in a different class. (This makes sense, since watermelon looks, tastes and feels so unlike other melons.) Watermelon cultivars have been established that can fit into a range of garden sizes. Some cultivars are even seedless. Note: Watermelon depends more than others on warm sunny weather (+75°F.) to grow. A few cultivars grow in slightly cooler climates, so check with a local nursery to see what types can grow in your area. See Melons for details on growing.

INSECT CONTROL

Besides the pests in the Melons entry, watermelons are vulnerable to aphids and squash vine borers. Deter aphids by planting French marigolds, which attract aphid predators. Squash vine borers are white caterpillars about one inch long. See Summer-Winter Squash for how to control borers.

TIPS

Watermelon is ripe when it sounds hollow after knocking on it. Store in a cool, shady place to ensure they last as long as they can (2-3 weeks).

Wheatgrass

HEALTH POWER

Wheatgrass juice or powder is a great low-calorie addition to the diet. It gives substantial vitamin C, iron and phytonutrients with little risk of adverse effects and a high potential for benefit. Within alternative medicine, wheatgrass has its strong proponents who tout its strength and versatility as a remedy. Some say wheatgrass gives them energy (by increasing metabolism), helps improve oxygen delivery to the cells (due to chlorophyll acting like hemoglobin in blood), boosts their immune system, helps improve skin conditions and wound healing (when drunk and applied topically), inhibits cancer cell development (especially liver cancer from the chlorophyll content), treats ulcerative colitis (inflammation of the colon), treats arthritis, prevents tooth decay (by holding in the mouth for 5 minutes), relieves constipation, detoxifies the blood (through high antioxidant behavior), decreases blood pressure and improves digestion. Little research has been done to support these statements. Still, give it a try and see how it makes you feel.

VITAMIN & MINERAL

Vitamins – C and traces
Minerals – Iron and traces

DISEASE PREVENTION

Drinking a shot of wheatgrass juice regularly may provide relief from or prevent the onset of rheumatoid and osteoarthritis, asthma, ulcers, heart disease, eczema, psoriasis and liver cancer. The American Cancer Society says it knows of no scientific evidence that wheatgrass can cure cancer or any disease after its onset. Wheatgrass, with its beneficial nutrients, may help alleviate symptoms and prevent the onset of many conditions.

HOW TO GROW

Growing wheatgrass is easy. It prefers a partly shady location, good air circulation and a temperature range of 60-75°F. This makes it an ideal candidate for indoor growing and some outdoor growing in the spring and fall. Get a growing tray and organic wheat seed from a local nursery. Soak seeds for 12 hours in a container throughout the day before planting. Rinse the seeds well and let them drain overnight. The next day, put about an inch of soil mixed with planting mix in the growing tray, dampening it by spraying it lightly as you spread the soil. Spread the wheatgrass seed on top of the soil. Water the tray with a spray bottle or a flexible spray hose from the sink. Cover the tray with an unbleached paper towel or another perforated lid (like an upside down growing tray) and spray the towel. Keep damp for 3-4 days. Generally, water once in the morning and once at night for the seed to germinate. When the seedlings reach a height of 1.5 inches, remove the paper towel or other cover and place in indirect sunlight. Temperature, humidity and air circulation will determine how frequently to water. Look underneath the tray. If the bottom is wet, do not water. A temperature of 60-75°F. is best. Harvest the wheatgrass as needed when it reaches 6-7 inches tall. Cut just above soil level and any sign of mold. Store the tray in a cool place to preserve it longer. You can juice the cuttings, dry and crush them to make powder or blend with water and strain out the foliage.

INSECT CONTROL

Insects are not usually a problem for wheatgrass, especially if grown inside. Good air circulation and warm temperatures help prevent mold forming.

TIPS

Keep the wheatgrass seed moist to achieve good germination.

Index